Dedication

*This manual is dedicated to the members of that unselfish organization
of men and women who hold devotion to duty
above personal risk, who count on sincerity of service above
personal comfort and convenience, who strive unceasingly to find
better ways of protecting the lives, homes and property
of their fellow citizens from the ravages of fire and other
disasters ...* **The Firefighters of All Nations**.

Dear Firefighter:

The International Fire Service Training Association (IFSTA) is an organization that exists
for the purpose of serving firefighters' training needs. Fire Protection Publications is the
publisher of IFSTA materials. Fire Protection Publications staff members participate in the
National Fire Protection Association and the International Association of Fire Chiefs.
If you need additional information concerning our organization or assistance with manual
orders, contact:

> **Customer Services**
> **Fire Protection Publications**
> **Oklahoma State University**
> **Stillwater, OK 74078-0118**
> **1 (800) 654-4055**

For assistance with training materials, recommended material for inclusion in a manual,
or questions on manual content, contact:

> **Technical Services**
> **Fire Protection Publications**
> **Oklahoma State University**
> **Stillwater, OK 74078-0118**
> **(405) 744-5723**

NOTICE

The questions in this study guide are taken from the information in the second edition of **Hazardous Materials For First Responders**, an IFSTA-validated manual. The questions are *not validated test questions and are not intended to be duplicated or used for certification or promotional examinations*; this guide is intended to be used as a tool for studying the information presented in **Hazardous Materials For First Responders.**

Table Of Contents

Preface

This study guide is designed to help the reader understand and remember the material presented in IFSTA's **Hazardous Materials For First Responders**, second edition. It identifies important information and concepts from each chapter and provides questions to help the reader study and retain this information. In addition, the study guide serves as an excellent resource for individuals preparing for certification or promotional examinations.

When used properly, this study guide ensures a better understanding of the knowledge and skills required by

- NFPA 471 *Recommended Practice for Responding to Hazardous Materials Incidents,*

- NFPA 472, *Standard for Professional Competence of Responders to Hazardous Materials Incidents,*

- NFPA 473, *Standard for Competencies for EMS Personnel Responding to Hazardous Materials Incidents,*

- 29 CFR 1910.120 *Hazardous Waste Operation and Emergency Response,* and

- 29 CFR 1910.1200 *Hazard Communications.*

It is sincerely hoped that these materials will be of value to those individuals who find themselves the first responders to hazardous materials incidents.

Much time and effort go into the design, development, layout, and printing of any publication. This **Study Guide For Hazardous Materials For First Responders** is no exception. I would like to extend a special thank-you to Max McRae, District Chief, Houston Fire Department, for his assistance in reviewing materials. Thank-you also to the following members of the Fire Protection Publications staff whose contributions made possible the technical accuracy and visual appeal of this publication.

Michael Wieder, Senior Publications Editor
Carol Smith, Senior Publications Editor
Ann Moffat, Graphic Designer Analyst
Desa Porter, Senior Graphic Designer
Shari Downs, Graphic Designer

Susan S. Walker
Coordinator of Instructional Development

How To Use This Book

This study guide is designed to be used in conjunction with and as a supplement to the second edition of the IFSTA manual **Hazardous Materials For First Responders**. The questions in this guide are designed to help you remember information and to make you think — they are *not* designed to trick or mislead you. To derive the maximum learning experience from these materials, use the following procedure:

Step 1: Read one chapter at a time in the **Hazardous Materials For First Responders** manual. After reading the chapter, underline or highlight important terms, topics, and subject matter in that chapter.

Step 2: Open the study guide to the corresponding chapter. Answer all of the questions in the study guide for that chapter. You may have to refer to the glossary for terms that appear in context but are not defined. After you have defined terms and answered all questions possible, check your answers with those in the answer section at the end of the study guide.

NOTE: *Do not* answer each question and then immediately check the answer for the correct response.

If you find that you have answered any question incorrectly, find the explanation of the answer in the **Hazardous Materials for First Responders** manual. The number in parentheses after each answer in the answer section identifies the page on which the answer or term can be found. Correct any incorrect answers, and review material that was answered incorrectly.

Step 3: Go to the next chapter of the manual and repeat Steps 1 and 2.

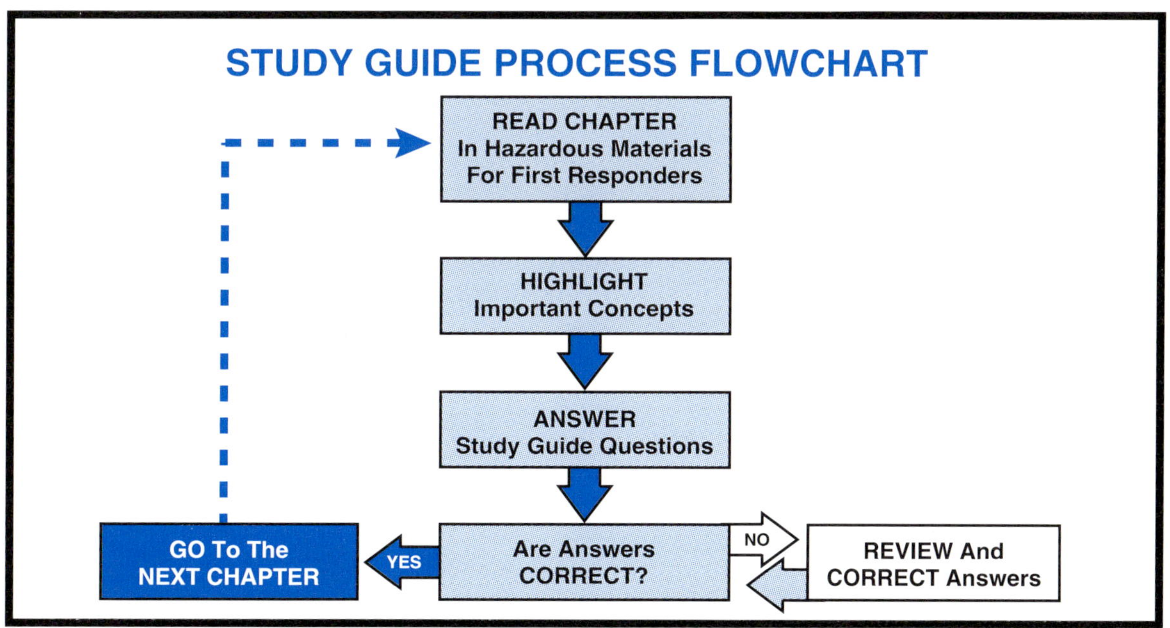

Chapter 1

Photo Courtesy of Scott D. Christiansen, Minot, N.D..

HAZ MAT

Introduction To Hazardous Materials

Introduction To Hazardous Materials | 1

DEFINITIONS OF KEY TERMS

Define each of the following terms.

1. Hazardous material *(As defined by the U.S. Department of Transportation in 49 CFR 171.8)*

2. Dangerous good *(As defined by the Canadian Transportation Commission)*

3. Hazardous waste *(As defined by the U.S. Department of Transportation in 49 CFR 171.8)*

4. Hazardous substance *(As defined by 42 USC 9601, Comprehensive Environmental Response, Compensation and Liability Act, section 101[14])*

5. Hazardous chemical *(As defined by the Occupational Safety and Health Administration in 29 CFR 1910.1200)*

1

6. Extremely hazardous substance *(As defined by the Environmental Protection Agency in 40 CFR 355.20)*

7. Imminent

8. Pursuant

9. Awareness level

10. Operational level

11. Etiological

12. Repository

13. Jurisdiction

14. Rapport

____

____

TRUE/FALSE

Mark each of the following statements true (T) or false (F). Correct each incorrect statement.

15. ☐ T   ☐ F   Hazardous materials and hazardous goods are two different terms for the same thing.

____

____

16. ☐ T   ☐ F   CERCLA, Section 101(14) lists all petroleum and petroleum by-products as hazardous substances.

____

____

17. ☐ T   ☐ F   Extremely hazardous substances are listed and identified in Title III SARA, 1986.

____

____

18. ☐ T   ☐ F   Dangerous goods are listed and identified in CERCLA, Section 101(14).

____

____

19. ☐ T   ☐ F   Hazardous materials are found in every community and workplace — there are no exceptions.

____

____

20. ☐ T   ☐ F   Jurisdictions that do not have large manufacturing and storage facilities have no potential for haz mat emergencies.

____

____

1

21. ☐ T ☐ F   The three U.S. and Canadian government agencies that require that responders to haz mat incidents meet specific training standards are OSHA, HAZWOPER, and ANSI.

22. ☐ T ☐ F   In addition to government regulations, IFSTA has several standards that set requirements for personnel who respond to haz mat emergencies.

23. ☐ T ☐ F   A motor vehicle accident in which a truck loaded with hay overturns and its diesel fuel tanks begin to leak would be considered a major haz mat incident.

24. ☐ T ☐ F   The discovery of a clandestine drug lab would be considered a major haz mat incident.

25. ☐ T ☐ F   The first responder at the awareness level has the responsibility of containing the spill.

26. ☐ T ☐ F   The potential for a haz mat incident can exist any time during the life of the material.

27. ☐ T ☐ F   For many years hazardous waste has been improperly stored or disposed of.

28. ☐ T ☐ F   All first responders should adopt a policy of cautious assessment before taking action.

29. ☐ T   ☐ F   Fire service personnel trained in haz mat response are the only agencies certified to handle haz mat incidents.

____

____

MULTIPLE CHOICE

Circle the letter before the most appropriate response.

30. What term is defined as *Discarded materials regulated by the EPA because of public health and safety concerns?*
    A.   Hazardous material
    B.   Hazardous substance
    C.   Hazardous waste
    D.   Hazardous chemical

31. In which of the following fixed locations will hazardous materials be found?
    A.   Residence
    B.   Farm
    C.   Service station
    D.   All of the above

32. Which of the following is NOT a government agency that sets regulations requiring haz mat first responders to meet specific training standards?
    A.   NFPA
    B.   EPA
    C.   WHMIS
    D.   OSHA

33. What aspect of haz mat response is covered by NFPA 472?
    A.   Professional competence of responders to haz mat incidents
    B.   Recommended practices for responding to haz mat incidents
    C.   Classification and definition of hazardous materials
    D.   Competencies for EMS personnel responding to haz mat incidents

34. Which of the following issues related to hazardous materials is NOT regulated by law (government regulations)?
    A.   Inspection of fixed facilities
    B.   Accidents leading to incidents
    C.   Inspection and operation of fixed facilities
    D.   Use of the material

1

Identify the following acronyms and abbreviations.

35. OSHA ____

36. EPA ____

37. WHMIS ____

38. HAZWOPER ____

39. NFPA ____

40. DOT ____

41. CFR ____

42. CERCLA ____

43. SWDA ____

44. SARA ____

45. CHEMTREC ____

46. CANUTEC ____

Identify the following items.

47. Haz mat incident *(as opposed to any other emergency incident)* _______________

____

48. Flammable liquid ____

49. Heavy metal ____

50. Carcinogen ____

51. Mutagen ____

52. Teratogen ____

LISTING

53. List the five transportation modes used to move hazardous materials.

A. ____

B. ____

C. ____

D. ____

E. ____

54. List five ordinary locations in which hazardous materials will be encountered.

A. ____

B. ____

C. ____

D. ____

E. ____

55. List the six crucial areas in which a haz mat first responder needs to be skilled in order to take the actions necessary to protect people, the environment, and property from harm.

A. ____
   ____

B. ____
   ____

C. ____
   ____

D. ____
   ____

E. ____
   ____

F. ____
   ____

56. List three causes of haz mat incidents that cannot be regulated by law.

A. ____

B. ____

C. ____

1

57. List the seven issues related to hazardous materials that can be regulated by law.

A. ____

B. ____

C. ____

D. ____

E. ____

F. ____

G. ____

58. List the five operations that may have to be performed simultaneously at a haz mat incident.

A. ____

B. ____

C. ____

D. ____

E. ____

59. List five of the variables that must be taken into consideration during incident assessment.

A. ____

B. ____

C. ____

D. ____

E. ____

60. List five agencies that may be called upon to cooperatively handle a haz mat incident.

A. ____

B. ____

C. ____

D. ____

E. ____

SHORT ANSWER

Briefly answer each question in your own words.

61. What are the responsibilities of the two first responder levels?

    A. First responder awareness level

    ____

    ____

    ____

    ____

    B. First responder operational level

    ____

    ____

    ____

    ____

    ____

62. What two goals are achieved when agencies formulate their haz mat pre-incident plans together?

    A. ____

    B. ____

63. Why are awareness and operational level first responders not to exceed the responsibilities of their roles?

    ____

    ____

64. Why is it important that *every* haz mat emergency response be documented?

    ____

    ____

65. Discuss problems associated with the storage of hazardous materials.

    ____

    ____

    ____

    ____

Chapter 2

HAZ MAT

Properties Of Hazardous Materials

Properties Of Hazardous Materials

2

Define each of the following terms.

1. Acute

2. Asphyxiant

3. Avulsion

4. Biochemical

5. Chronic

6. Condensation

7. Congenital

8. Corrosive

2

9. Cryogen

____

____

10. Dehydration

____

____

11. Dyspnea

____

____

12. Evaporation

____

____

13. Flammability

____

____

14. Inert

____

____

15. Inhibit

____

____

16. Lethal

____

____

17. Metabolism

____

____

18. Olfactory

____

____

2

19. Radioactive

____

____

20. Reactivity

____

____

21. Stimulus

____

____

22. Suffocate

____

____

23. Thermal

____

____

24. Vapor pressure

____

____

TRUE/FALSE

Mark each of the following statements true (T) or false (F). Correct each false statement.

25. ☐ T ☐ F   Symptoms of heat exhaustion include lack of perspiration; hot, red, dry skin; and confusion.

____

____

26. ☐ T ☐ F   The first responder should drink plenty of carbonated beverages before and during operations.

____

____

2

27. ☐ T ☐ F The first responder should avoid liquids such as alcohol, coffee, and caffeinated drinks before working as these beverages can contribute to dehydration and heat stress.

____

____

28. ☐ T ☐ F Cryogens have the ability to instantly freeze materials, including human tissue, on contact.

____

____

29. ☐ T ☐ F Liquefied gases can cause freeze burns, which are treated like heat burns according to their severity.

____

____

30. ☐ T ☐ F Typically there will be pain associated with a base on contact.

____

____

31. ☐ T ☐ F Simple asphyxiants are also called *blood poisons*.

____

____

32. ☐ T ☐ F Internal exposure from alpha particles is the most common cause of radiation poisoning.

____

____

33. ☐ T ☐ F Radiation sickness, injury, and poisoning are infectious and contagious.

____

____

34. ☐ T ☐ F Beta radiation particles are about 1/7000 the size of alpha particles and have more penetrating power.

____

____

35. ☐ T ☐ F Alpha radiation particles have a negative electrical charge.

____

____

2

36. ☐ T   ☐ F   An external alpha particle cannot penetrate a sheet of paper used as a shield.

____

____

37. ☐ T   ☐ F   Very dense materials, such as lead, prohibit the penetration of gamma radiation.

____

____

38. ☐ T   ☐ F   Neutron radiation is most likely to be encountered in research laboratories.

____

____

39. ☐ T   ☐ F   In general, liquid hazardous materials pose more of a potential danger to first responders than do gaseous hazardous materials.

____

____

40. ☐ T   ☐ F   Some toxic substances, such as the cyanides, cannot be detected by the human sensory system because they are essentially odorless and colorless.

____

____

41. ☐ T   ☐ F   The higher the LC_{50} values, the more toxic a substance.

____

____

42. ☐ T   ☐ F   Flammable liquids do not burn.

____

____

43. ☐ T   ☐ F   Propane gas is lighter than air.

____

____

44. ☐ T   ☐ F   Many chemicals release a characteristic vapor cloud.

____

____

2

45. ☐ T   ☐ F   Most flammable liquids have specific gravities less than 1.0 and float on the surface of water.

____

____

MULTIPLE CHOICE

Circle the letter before the most appropriate response.

46. Which of the following is NOT a major chronic health hazard class?
    A. Carcinogen
    B. Mutagen
    C. Teratogen
    D. Allergen

47. From what type of thermal effect is the firefighter with muscle cramps, heavy perspiration, physical weakness, and moist skin most likely suffering?
    A. Heat exhaustion
    B. Heat cramps
    C. Heat rash
    D. Heat stroke

48. What is the recommended fluid intake to prevent or reduce the risk of dehydration and other effects of heat exposure?
    A. 7 ounces (200 ml) body-fluid-replenishment drink or water every 15 to 20 minutes
    B. Generous amount of water once an hour
    C. 12 ounces (375 ml) of salt water every 4 hours
    D. 8 ounces (250 ml) of sweetened, carbonated beverage or fruit juice every 30 minutes

49. Which of the following is NOT a cryogenic material, but instead, a liquefied gas?
    A. Propane
    B. LOX
    C. LNG
    D. Hydrogen

50. In haz mat situations, what is most likely to cause a striking injury to the responder?
    A. Exploding vehicle parts
    B. Collapsing building parts
    C. Exploding pressurized containers
    D. Contact between protective clothing and skin

51. Which word below is defined as *Chemical exposures that destroy or burn living tissues and have destructive effects on other materials*?
    A. Poisons
    B. Corrosives
    C. Cryogens
    D. Contagions

52. Which of the following is NOT a base?
    A. Caustic soda
    B. Potassium hydroxide
    C. Sodium carbonate
    D. Hydrogen chloride and water

53. Sudden deterioration, discoloration, or melting of equipment should cause the first responder to have serious safety concerns and suspect which of the following types of materials?
    A. Chemical asphyxiant
    B. Radiation exposure
    C. Corrosive chemical
    D. Etiological material

54. Which of the following is NOT a *simple* asphyxiant?
    A. Carbon monoxide
    B. Carbon dioxide
    C. Acetylene
    D. Methane

55. Which of the following is NOT a *chemical* asphyxiant?
    A. Toluene
    B. Carbon monoxide
    C. Methane
    D. Benzene

56. At which of the following facilities is there potential for radiation exposure?
    A. Supermarket
    B. Hospital
    C. Business supply store
    D. Pest control shop

57. Which of the following substances is impenetrable by gamma rays?
    A. Thick lead
    B. ⅛-inch (3 mm) aluminum
    C. Cardboard
    D. Paper

2

58. What type of radiation particles move at the speed of light?
    A. Alpha
    B. Beta
    C. Gamma
    D. Neutron

59. What type of radiation is controlled and used for X-rays?
    A. Alpha
    B. Beta
    C. Gamma
    D. Neutron

60. What type of radiation is most likely to be encountered in research laboratories?
    A. Alpha
    B. Beta
    C. Gamma
    D. Neutron

61. Which of the following is NOT a way to provide protection from external radiation during an emergency?
    A. Time
    B. Distance
    C. Shielding
    D. Showering

62. Which of the following statements about radiation protection is true?
    A. The longer the time exposure, the smaller the radiation dose.
    B. As the distance from the source doubles, the amount of radiation increases by the square of the distance.
    C. Responders wearing PPE and SCBA are generally protected from internal radiation.
    D. Showering immediately after exposure protects against penetrating forms of radiation.

63. How are most etiological hazards transmitted?
    A. Contact with body fluids
    B. Exposure to vapor clouds
    C. Penetration of radioactive particles
    D. Contact with hazardous chemicals

64. Which of the following is NOT a convulsant?
    A. Strychnine
    B. Dyspitoxin
    C. Carbamate
    D. Organophosphate

65. What is the ultimate problem associated with exposure to carcinogenic materials and other poisons?
    A. Unknown long-term effects
    B. Lack of cure for disease-producing results
    C. Immediate medical symptoms or injury
    D. Uncontrolled infection or contagion

66. Which of the following is NOT a mutagen?
    A. Radiation
    B. Benzene
    C. Arsenic
    D. Ethylene oxide

67. Which of the following is NOT a teratogen?
    A. Ethyl alcohol
    B. Chlorinated hydrocarbon
    C. Thalidomide
    D. Methly mercury

68. What entity establishes threshold limit values for hazardous materials?
    A. ACGIH
    B. OSHA
    C. NIOSH
    D. EPA

69. What percent concentration of flammable gas or vapor above the LEL is considered to have serious ignition potential?
    A. 4
    B. 6
    C. 8
    D. 10

70. What word below is defined as *Capable of undergoing spontaneous change*?
    A. Stimulation reaction
    B. Stable substance
    C. Unstable substance
    D. Decomposition process

2

Match routes of entry with their descriptions. Write the correct letters in the blanks.

71. _______ Process of taking materials into the body through the mouth by means other than breathing

72. _______ Process of taking materials into the body by breathing through the nose or mouth

73. _______ Process of taking materials into the body through the skin or eyes

74. _______ Process of taking materials into the body through a puncture or stick with a needle

A. Absorption

B. Inhalation

C. Ingestion

D. Injection

Match materials with their reactivity hazards. Write the correct letters in the blanks.

75. _______ React or ignite on contact with air

76. _______ Decompose with little or no outside stimulus; capable of undergoing spontaneous change

77. _______ React in varying degrees when either mixed with water or exposed to humid air

78. _______ Ignite when coming into contact with each other

A. Unstable substance

B. Hypergolic materials

C. Pyrophoric materials

D. Water-reactive materials

Match the following toxins with the body organs they affect. Write the correct letters in the blanks.

79. _______ Kidneys

80. _______ Blood

81. _______ Central nervous system

82. _______ Liver

A. Nephrotoxin

B. Hepatoxin

C. Neurotoxin

D. Hematoxin

2

Match basic types of radiation with their descriptions. Write the correct letters in the blanks.

83. _______ Electromagnetic form of penetrating radiation that bears no particular electrical charge, and in which the radiation rays arise from a complete atom

84. _______ Radiation consisting of particles having a large mass and a positive electrical charge

85. _______ Electromagnetic form of penetrating radiation that bears no particular electrical charge, and in which the radiation rays arise solely from the nucleus of the atom

86. _______ Radiation consisting of very small negatively charged particles

87. _______ Highly penetrating type of radiation with a large physical mass but with no electrical charge

A. Alpha radiation

B. Beta radiation

C. X-ray radiation

D. Gamma radiation

E. Neutron radiation

Match types of hazards with their general effects on the exposed body. Write the correct letters in the blanks. Effects column is continued on the next page.

88. _______ Bodily injury as a result of direct contact with an object

89. _______ Permanent and irreversible conditions that appear over the long term and may affect either the exposed persons or their children

90. _______ Severe, disabling disease

91. _______ Freezing or freeze burns of human tissue

92. _______ Injury as a result of portions of the body rubbing against an abrasive surface

93. _______ Allergic reaction after repeated exposure

94. _______ A range of high-temperature-related health threats caused by fluctuations in the body's core temperature

95. _______ Reduced oxygen flow to the lungs and body generally leading to suffocation

A. Etiologic hazard

B. Chronic health hazard

C. Cold exposure

D. Heat exposure

E. Poison

F. Asphyxiant

G. Radiation hazard

H. Corrosive

I. Mechanical striking hazard

J. Mechanical friction hazard

K. Sensitizer/allergen

L. Irritant

M. Convulsant

2

96. ______ Damage to respiratory, circulatory, digestive, or nervous systems, organs, and other body parts, possibly causing death

97. ______ Somatic and genetic effects

98. ______ Aggrevation of respiratory system but may also cause temporary but severe inflammation of the eyes or skin

99. ______ Seizures that may result in death from asphyxiation or exhaustion

100. ______ Chemical burns or chemical destruction of living tissue

IDENTIFICATION

Identify the following abbreviations and acronyms.

101. ACGIH____

102. ppm ____

103. mg/m^3 ____

104. mg/L ____

105. TLV-TWA ____

106. TLV-STEL ______________________________________

107. TLV-C ____

108. PEL ____

109. LD_{50} ____

110. LC_{50} ____

111. IDLH ____

Identify each of the following terms associated with exposure safety limits.

112. Threshhold Limit Values (TLV) ________________________

113. TLV/Time-Weighted Average __________________________

114. TLV/Short-Term Exposure Limit _______________________

2

115. TLV/Ceiling Level ____

116. Permissible Exposure Limit __ ______________________________________

117. Lethal Dose ____

118. Lethal Concentration ______________________________________

119. Immediately Dangerous to Life and Health ______________________

____

Identify each of the following properties and factors related to flammability hazards.

120. Flashpoint ____

121. Firepoint ____

122. Autoignition temperature ________________________________

123. Flammable (explosive) range ____________________________

124. Specific gravity ____

125. Vapor density ____

126. Boiling point ____

127. Miscibility ____

Provide the requested information.

128. Identify the flashpoints for each of the following fuel classes.

    A. Flammable liquids ____________________________________

    B. Combustible liquids __________________________________

    C. Flammable gases ______________________________________

    D. Solids (such as napthalene) ____________________________

LISTING

129. List the symptoms of heat cramps.

    A. ____

    B. ____

    C. ____

    D. ____

2

130. List the symptoms of heat exhaustion.

    A. ____

    B. ____

    C. ____

    D. ____

    E. ____

131. List the symptoms of heatstroke.

    A. ____

    B. ____

    C. ____

    D. ____

    E. ____

    F. ____

    G. ____

    H. ____

    I. ____

    J. ____

132. List six ways in which first responders can protect themselves by preventing or reducing the effects of heat exposure.

    A. ____

    B. ____

    C. ____

    D. ____

    E. ____

    F. ____

133. List the symptoms of external corrosive exposures.

    A. ____

    B. ____

    C. ____

    D. ____

2

134. List four examples of simple asphyxiants.

    A. ____

    B. ____

    C. ____

    D. ____

135. List four examples of chemical asphyxiants.

    A. ____

    B. ____

    C. ____

    D. ____

136. List three examples of diseases associated with etiological events.

    A. ____

    B. ____

    C. ____

137. List two examples of convulsants.

    A. ____

    B. ____

138. List five examples of known or suspected carcinogens.

    A. ____

    B. ____

    C. ____

    D. ____

    E. ____

139. List two examples of mutagens.

    A. ____

    B. ____

140. List four examples of teratogens.

    A. ____

    B. ____

    C. ____

    D. ____

2

141. List three toxic products of combustion.

A. ____

B. ____

C. ____

142. List two examples for each of the following classes of materials.

A. Unstable material

____

____

B. Hypergolic material

____

____

C. Pyrophoric material

____

____

D. Water-reactive material

____

____

LABELING

143. Label the parts of the respiratory tract. Write the correct names in the blanks corresponding to the lettered parts.

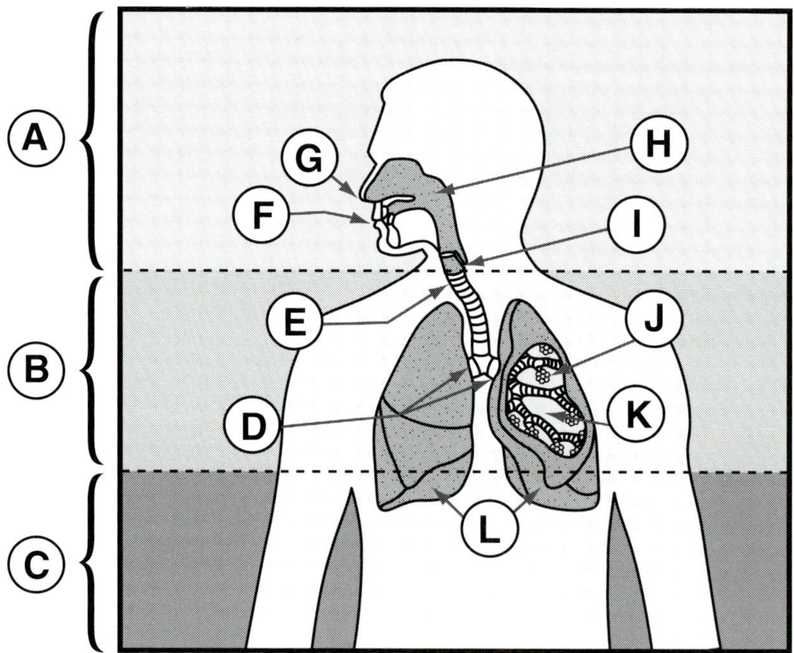

A. _______________________________   G. _______________________________

B. _______________________________   H. _______________________________

C. _______________________________   I. _______________________________

D. _______________________________   J. _______________________________

E. _______________________________   K. _______________________________

F. _______________________________   L. _______________________________

SHORT ANSWER

Briefly answer each question in your own words.

144. Distinguish among carcinogens, mutagens, and teratogens.

    A. Carcinogen ____

    B. Mutagen ____

    C. Teratogen ____

145. Distinguish between somatic and genetic effects of radiation exposure.

    A. Somatic effect ____

    B. Genetic effect ____

146. Compare the effects on body tissue of acids and bases.

    A. Acids ____

    ____

    B. Bases ____

    ____

147. Compare the ways that simple asphyxiants and chemical asphyxiants react on the body.

    A. Simple asphyxiant _____________________________________

    ____

    B. Chemical asphyxiant ___________________________________

    ____

148. Distinguish among the causes and symptoms of the following effects of radiation exposure.

    A. Radiation sickness _____________________________________

    ____

    B. Radiation injury _______________________________________

    ____

    C. Radiation poisoning ____________________________________

    ____

149. Explain the following radiation protection strategies.

    A. Time ____

    ____

    B. Distance ____

    ____

2

C. Shielding ____

____

150. Distinguish between polar solvents and hydrocarbons.

A. Polar solvent ____

____

B. Hydrocarbon ____

____

151. Explain the differences between hypergolic materials and pyrophoric materials.

A. Hypergolic ____

____

B. Pyrophoric ____

____

Photo Courtesy of Scott D. Christiansen, Minot, N.D..

HAZ MAT

Recognizing And Identifying Hazardous Materials

Recognizing And Identifying Hazardous Materials | 3

Define each of the following terms.

1. Carboy

2. Consignee

3. Contingency

4. Frangible

5. Intermodal

6. Outage

7. Polymerization

8. Prilled

3

9. Tare

____

____

10. Volatile

____

____

Mark each of the following statements true (T) or false (F). Correct each false statement.

11. ☐ T ☐ F Shipped cryogenic materials must be placarded regardless of quantity.

____

____

12. ☐ T ☐ F Chlorine requires placarding only if it is shipped in excess of 1,000 pounds.

____

____

13. ☐ T ☐ F Flammable solids are shipped in marine tankers.

____

____

14. ☐ T ☐ F Radioactive materials are the only hazardous materials shipped in lead-shielded containers.

____

____

15. ☐ T ☐ F Wooden and fiberboard boxes are used only as the outside packaging for inside containers of hazardous materials.

____

____

16. ☐ T ☐ F Explosives and corrosives are the only hazardous materials shipped in metal kegs.

____

____

3

17. ☐ T   ☐ F   In NFPA 704 markings, the health hazard rating appears at the three o'clock position.

____

____

18. ☐ T   ☐ F   The first responder must never rely solely on informal methods of identification to arrive at decisions that may put human life at risk.

____

____

19. ☐ T   ☐ F   Using the human senses indiscriminately to detect the presence of hazardous materials is both unreliable and unsafe.

____

____

20. ☐ T   ☐ F   At the onset of physical symptoms of chemical exposure, those people exposed should be immediately transported to a medical facility.

____

____

21. ☐ T   ☐ F   All chemical exposures result in immediate and very apparent symptoms.

____

____

22. ☐ T   ☐ F   Explosives are listed individually in the *ERG* by identification number.

____

____

23. ☐ T   ☐ F   Highlighted entries in the *ERG* indicate that the material may be shipped under a generic name.

____

____

24. ☐ T   ☐ F   When first responders using Canada's *IERG* cannot identify a hazardous material by its identification number, name, placard, or container shape, they should refer to Guide 11.

____

____

3

25. ☐ T ☐ F The placarding/labeling system used by Canada's *IERG* is reciprocal to that used in the United States.

____

____

26. ☐ T ☐ F Each *IERG* Guide lists initial evacuation distances for large spills and fires.

____

____

27. ☐ T ☐ F The *IERG* and the *ERG* are scheduled to be combined into a single guide in 1995.

____

____

28. ☐ T ☐ F Anyone who offers a hazardous material for transportation must enter on the shipping document a 24-hour emergency response telephone number.

____

____

29. ☐ T ☐ F CHEMTREC/CANUTEC notifies shippers of the incident, will FAX information to the first responder, and will facilitate telephone conference calls between responders and the shipper.

____

____

30. ☐ T ☐ F After learning of a haz mat accident, the shipper may decide to activate its own response team or to coordinate other mutual aid assistance.

____

____

31. ☐ T ☐ F U.S. and Canadian material safety data sheets are virtually identical and interchangeable.

____

____

32. ☐ T ☐ F The first responder should consult a minimum of four resources for information about a material.

____

____

33. ☐ T ☐ F   A hazardous material is most easily identified after it is released from its container.

34. ☐ T ☐ F   Transported hazardous materials and those manufactured, stored, processed, or used at fixed facilities are subject to the same regulations.

35. ☐ T ☐ F   The NFPA 704 system identifies the specific chemical or chemicals that may be present.

36. ☐ T ☐ F   Class 7 Radioactive I, II, and III labels *must always* contain text.

37. ☐ T ☐ F   Some states do not require placarding of haz mat shipments when the origin and destination are both within the state.

38. ☐ T ☐ F   Some refrigerated boxcars carry up to 500 gallons (2 000 L) of gasoline for cooling system power generation equipment.

39. ☐ T ☐ F   A white railcar with a red horizontal stripe around it and two vertical red stripes 3 feet (1 m) from each end always hauls hydrogen chloride (hydrochloric acid).

40. ☐ T ☐ F   The first responder need only identify the type of cargo tank truck to make a positive identification of the hazardous material it is transporting.

3

41. ☐ T   ☐ F   Materials may be transported in a liquid or solid state at temperatures at or above boiling.

42. ☐ T   ☐ F   When a pressurized tank railcar transports flammable gases, it is covered by a thermal jacket or by a sprayed-on protective coating.

43. ☐ T   ☐ F   If a tank railcar is classified as "DOT-115," it is a pressurized railcar.

44. ☐ T   ☐ F   A nonpressure tank railcar that transports hazardous materials is also known as a general service or low-pressure tank car.

45. ☐ T   ☐ F   A nonpressure tank railcar may carry nonhazardous materials such as molasses or tomato paste.

46. ☐ T   ☐ F   Most tank cars that carry cryogenic liquids are either loaded or unloaded from the top and have no plumbing underneath.

47. ☐ T   ☐ F   Hazardous materials transported by boxcar, hopper car, or other freight cars cannot be identified by the outer appearance of the car.

48. ☐ T   ☐ F   General service tank railcars are easily distinguishable from those transporting hazardous materials.

49. ☐ T   ☐ F   The EPA requires a warning label on any containers, transformers, or capacitors that contain PCBs.

50. ☐ T ☐ F Companies that bury pipeline carrying hazardous materials must mark the pipeline at each railroad crossing, at each public road crossing, and with a sufficient number of markers along the rest of the pipeline to identify the pipe's location.

____

____

51. ☐ T ☐ F The first responder must be able to operate and interpret the readings of monitoring instruments used to detect the presence of hazardous materials.

____

____

MULTIPLE CHOICE

Circle the letter before the most appropriate response.

52. Which type of material requires placarding regardless of quantity?
    A. Corrosive materials
    B. 1.1, 1.2, and 1.3 explosives
    C. Organic peroxides
    D. Oxidizers

53. Which material only requires placarding if in excess of 1,000 pounds?
    A. 1.1, 1.2, and 1.3 explosives
    B. Uranium hexafluoride, low-specific activity
    C. PGI, PIH poisons
    D. 4.2 Combustibles

54. What hazardous material must be placarded regardless of quantity?
    A. PG II poisons
    B. 1.6 explosives
    C. Dangerous when wet materials
    D. Corrosive materials

55. Which of the following is NOT a shipping container for compressed gas?
    A. Metal keg
    B. Portable tank
    C. Cylinder
    D. Barge

56. In what type of container may etiological agents be shipped?
    A. Fiberboard or wooden boxes
    B. Glass carboy in plywood drum or box
    C. Cylinder
    D. Lead-shielded container

3

57. In what type of container may radioactive material be shipped?
    A.   Fiberboard or wooden boxes
    B.   Glass carboy in plywood drum or box
    C.   Cylinder
    D.   Lead-shielded container

58. Which material is shipped only in glass carboys in plywood drums or boxes?
    A.   Oxidizer
    B.   Organic peroxide
    C.   Corrosive material
    D.   Poisonous material

59. What is the primary objective of the *ERG/IERG*?
    A.   To direct first responders to the appropriate Guide page as quickly as possible upon their arrival at the haz mat incident
    B.   To provide step-by-step actions that first responders must take to resolve any possible haz mat incident safely
    C.   To index the hazards associated with known hazardous materials
    D.   To provide a directory of all known resources that can be called upon to assist the first responder in safely resolving the haz mat incident

60. How many Initial Action Guides are there in the *ERG*?
    A.   1,000
    B.   575
    C.   77
    D.   272

61. What Guide are first responders directed to if the hazardous material is identified as Division 1.1, 1.2, 1.3, 1.5, or 1.6 explosive?
    A.   Guide 11
    B.   Guide 50
    C.   Guide 46
    D.   Guide 26

62. What Guide are first responders directed to if the hazardous material is identified as Division 1.4 explosive?
    A.   Guide 11
    B.   Guide 50
    C.   Guide 46
    D.   Guide 26

63. What does the first section of the *IERG* contain?
    A.   Materials listed alphabetically by name
    B.   Materials listed by their identification numbers
    C.   Placards and labels chart
    D.   Transportation identification chart

64. When shipping papers are available, who should the first responder call first (if possible) to gain information about a shipment of hazardous materials?
    A. Shipper's emergency response center
    B. Chemical manufacturer or shipper
    C. *ERG/IERG*
    D. NRC

65. Who mandates the content of material safety data sheets (MSDS)?
    A. Local and federal government
    B. NRA
    C. NFPA
    D. OSHA

66. For which of the following is the NFPA 704 system designed?
    A. Transportation
    B. General public use
    C. Commercial, manufacturing, institutional, and other fixed facilities
    D. Nonemergency occupational exposures

67. Which of the following is NOT a DOT Class 4 division?
    A. Flammable solid
    B. Flammable liquid
    C. Spontaneously combustible material
    D. Dangerous when wet material

68. What type of document does DOT/TC specify must accompany all shipments of hazardous waste?
    A. Uniform hazardous waste manifest
    B. Unified hazardous waste waybill
    C. Combined hazardous waste weight and bill of lading
    D. Unilateral hazardous waste warranty

69. Which of the following hazardous materials does NOT require a placard?
    A. Infectious substances
    B. Combustible liquids
    C. Flammable solids
    D. Nonflammable gas

70. How may a freight container, unit load device, transport vehicle, or railcar that contains nonbulk packaging with two or more categories of hazardous materials be placarded?
    A. With an appropriate placard for each material
    B. With the word HAZARDOUS (in the U.S.) or HAZARD (in Canada)
    C. With the word DANGEROUS (in the U.S.) or DANGER (in Canada)
    D. Problem will not arise as different categories of hazardous materials cannot be mixed in shipment

3

71. What word may be substituted for FLAMMABLE on a placard displayed on a cargo tank or on a portable tank used to transport gasoline by highway?
    A. FUEL
    B. FUEL OIL
    C. VEHICLE FUEL
    D. GASOLINE

72. What word may be used in place of the word COMBUSTIBLE on a placard displayed on a cargo tank or on a portable tank used to transport fuel oil by highway?
    A. FUEL
    B. FUEL OIL
    C. VEHICLE FUEL
    D. GASOLINE

73. What types of hazardous materials require that the words POISON GAS-RESIDUE or POISON-RESIDUE be placed on a placard with a square background affixed to rail tank cars?
    A. Division 2.4, Hazard Zone A *or* Division 1.4, Packing Group I, Hazard Zone B materials
    B. Division 4.2, Hazard Zone B *or* Division 4.1, Packing Group II, Hazard Zone A materials
    C. Division 3.2, Hazard Zone B *or* Division 5.1, Packing Group III, Hazard Zone A materials
    D. Division 2.3, Hazard Zone A *or* Division 6.1, Packing Group I, Hazard Zone A materials

74. What word must appear on placards affixed to any rail transport vehicle or freight container containing lading that has been fumigated or treated with a poisonous liquid, solid, or gas?
    A. TOXIN
    B. PESTICIDE
    C. FUMIGATED
    D. POISON

75. Which of the following is NOT a distinguishing feature of an atmospheric pressure cargo tank truck?
    A. Elliptical tank with longitudinal rollover protection
    B. Manhole assemblies and vapor recovery valves on top for each compartment
    C. Valving and unloading control box under tank
    D. Exterior stiffening rings

76. Which cargo tank carrier transports gases that have been liquefied through compression?
    A. MC-307/DOT-407
    B. MC-331
    C. MC-312/DOT-412
    D. MC-338

77. Which of the following is a distinguishing characteristic of a corrosive liquid cargo tank carrier?
    A. Bolted manhole at rear
    B. Discoloration around loading/unloading area
    C. Large hemispherical heads on both ends
    D. Christmas tree vent outside flash box on top of tank

78. Which of the following is NOT a distinguishing feature of a high-pressure cargo tank carrier?
    A. Flange-type rupture disk vent either inside or outside splash guard
    B. Guard cage around bottom loading/unloading piping
    C. Uninsulated tanks, single-shell vessels usually painted white
    D. Permanent markings such as FLAMMABLE GAS, COMPRESSED GAS

79. Which cargo tank carrier has the manifold enclosed at the rear?
    A. Cryogenic liquid carrier
    B. Dry bulk carrier
    C. Compressed gas trailer (tube trailer)
    D. High-pressure carrier

80. What marking is affixed to the packaging of elevated-temperature materials transported in bulk packaging?
    A. MOLTEN
    B. HIGH IGNITION HAZARD
    C. BURN HAZARD
    D. HOT

81. Which of the following would NOT be an identification marking on an intermodal tank?
    A. Initials (reporting marks) and tank number
    B. Country code
    C. Size/type code
    D. UN identification number

3

Match NFPA 704 rating numbers with associated health hazards. Write the correct letters in the blanks.

82. ________ Materials that on exposure cause irritation but only minor residual injury

83. ________ Materials that on very short exposure could cause death or major residual injury

84. ________ Materials that on exposure under fire conditions would offer no hazard beyond that of ordinary combustible material

85. ________ Materials that on short exposure could cause serious temporary or residual injury

86. ________ Materials that on intense or continued, but not chronic, exposure could cause temporary incapacitation or possible residual injury

A. 4
B. 3
C. 2
D. 1
E. 0

Match NFPA 704 material rating numbers with associated flammability characteristics. Write the correct letters in the blanks.

87. ________ Materials that will not burn

88. ________ Materials that must be preheated before ignition can occur

89. ________ Liquids and solids that can be ignited under almost all ambient temperature conditions

90. ________ Materials that must be moderately heated or exposed to relatively high ambient temperatures before ignition can occur

91. ________ Materials that will rapidly or completely vaporize at atmospheric pressure and normal ambient temperature, or that are readily dispersed in air and that will burn readily

A. 4
B. 3
C. 2
D. 1
E. 0

Match NFPA 704 material rating numbers with associated reactivity. Write the correct letters in the blanks.

92. ______ Materials that in themselves are capable of detonation, explosive decomposition, or reaction but require a strong initiating source, or those materials that must be heated under confinement before initiation, or react explosively with water

93. ______ Materials that in themselves are readily capable of detonation, explosive decomposition, or reaction at normal temperatures and pressures

94. ______ Materials that in themselves are normally stable — even under fire exposure conditions — and which are not reactive with water

95. ______ Materials that readily undergo violent chemical change at elevated temperatures and pressures, react violently with water, or may form explosive mixtures with water

96. ______ Materials that in themselves are normally stable, but which can become unstable at elevated temperatures and pressures

A. 4

B. 3

C. 2

D. 1

E. 0

Match sections of the *ERG* with their page color codes. Write the correct letters in the blanks.

97. ______ UN/NA Identification Number Index

98. ______ Name of Material Index

99. ______ Initial Action Guides

100. ______ Placard Table

101. ______ Table of Initial Isolation and Protective Action Distances

102. ______ Guide 11

A. Yellow

B. White (no border)

C. Green

D. Blue

E. Orange

3

Match sections of the *IERG* with their page color codes. Write the correct letters in the blanks.

103. _______ PIN Index

104. _______ Material Name Index

105. _______ Initial Action Response Guides

106. _______ Chart of Placards and Labels

107. _______ Rail Car and Road Trailer Identification Chart

108. _______ Guide 01

A. Orange
B. Green
C. Yellow
D. White

Match *ERG* sections/indexes with their use descriptions. Write the correct letters in the blanks.

109. _______ Use to identify a material that cannot be specifically identified by using shipping papers, numbered placard, or identification numbers

110. _______ Use to identify the appropriate guide page for a material whose name from the shipping document is known or has been identified

111. _______ Use to identify the appropriate guide page for a material whose number is known or has been identified

112. _______ Use as a guide for initial actions to take for materials that cannot be identified using any of the index methods

113. _______ Use to determine the initial actions to take upon arrival at the haz mat incident, as well as to determine potential hazards, fire instructions, leak or spill guidance, and first aid procedures

114. _______ Use to identify protective measures needed for highlighted poison and inhalation risks

A. UN/NA Identification Number Index
B. Material Name Index
C. Initial Action Guides
D. Placard Table
E. Table of Initial Isolation and Protective Action Distances
F. Guide 11

Match types of fixed facility haz mat storage containers with their descriptions. Write the correct letters in the blanks. Descriptions are continued on the next page.

115. _______ Large-capacity aboveground holding tank commonly used to store flammable and combustible liquids, particularly petroleum products; roof slides up and down the tank walls and sits atop the liquid, eliminating a potentially dangerous vapor space

116. _______ Round tank with pressure-relief valve on top; designed to store liquid or gaseous commodities such as LPG, methane, propane and other light gases; may also be used to store flammable liquids such as gasoline or crude oil or domestic water

117. _______ Usually used to store volatile liquids; roof is liquid- or fabric-sealed and designed to move up or down with changes in vapor pressure

118. _______ Vertical storage tank with domed top, the underside of which contains a flexible diaphragm that moves in conjunction with changes of vapor pressure; used to store combustible liquids of medium volatility or nonhazardous materials such as molasses or fertilizer blends

119. _______ Stores flammable, combustible, or corrosive liquids; roof-to-shell seam designed to break if container becomes overpressurized

120. _______ Nonpressurized aboveground steel tank supported by unsupported steel struts or stilts; used for bulk storage in conjunction with fuel-dispensing operations

121. _______ Steel or fiberglass tank designed to be buried, primarily at gasoline stations; has aboveground fill and vent connections

122. _______ Large rounded tank with pressure-relief valve at top and with bulging, ribbed sections held together by a series of internal ties and supports that reduce stress on the external shell; designed to store liquid or gaseous commodities such as LPG, meth-

A. Cryogenic-liquid storage tank

B. Lifter roof atmospheric tank

C. Floating roof atmospheric tank

D. Spheroid low-pressure tank

E. Ordinary cone roof atmospheric tank

F. Horizontal tank pressure vessel

G. Vapordome roof atmospheric tank

H. Sphere tank pressure vessel

I. Internal floating roof atmospheric tank

J. Noded spheroid low-pressure tank

K. Underground storage tank

L. Horizontal atmospheric tank

3

ane, propane and other light gases; may also be used to store flammable liquids such as gasoline or crude oil or domestic water

123. _______ Long, low-pressurized vessel with rounded ends commonly found at facilities that dispense fuel gas to the public; may be used to store propane, LNG, CNG, butane, ethane, ammonia, sulfur dioxide, chlorine, or hydrogen chloride

124. _______ Ball-like noninsulated tank often supported off the ground with concrete or steel legs; usually painted white to reduce internal vaporization; commonly used to store liquefied petroleum gases

125. _______ Insulated, vacuum-jacketed tank with safety relief valves and rupture discs used for storing hazardous materials such as nitrogen or LOX

126. _______ Used primarily to store flammable liquids; has fixed cone roof and either pan or deck-type float inside tank that rides directly on product surface

Match federal agencies involved in the regulation of hazardous materials/wastes with their functions. Write the correct letters in the blanks.

127. _______ Regulates the possession, use, and transport of radioactive materials

128. _______ Regulates companies — such as electric companies — that generate power

129. _______ Shares overall regulatory authority with TDG

130. _______ Regulates the health and safety of first responders and workers employed by shippers and carriers of hazardous materials

131. _______ Establishes requirements for the transportation of hazardous substances and wastes

132. _______ Shares overall regulatory authority with DOT

A. Department of Energy

B. Department of Transportation

C. Environmental Protection Agency

D. Nuclear Regulatory Commission

E. Occupational Safety and Health Administration

F. Transport Development Group

Match hazardous materials with their UN identification system classes. Write the correct letters in the blanks.

133. ______ Miscellaneous

134. ______ Poisons and infectious substances

135. ______ Corrosives

136. ______ Explosives

137. ______ Gases

138. ______ Flammable solids

139. ______ Radioactive substances

140. ______ Flammable liquids

141. ______ Oxidizers

A. Class 1
B. Class 2
C. Class 3
D. Class 4
E. Class 5
F. Class 6
G. Class 7
H. Class 8
I. Class 9

Match descriptions of DOT Class 1 explosion hazards with their division numbers. Write the correct letters in the blanks.

142. ______ Having a fire hazard and either a minor blast hazard or a minor projection hazard or both but not a mass explosion hazard

143. ______ Extremely insensitive articles that do not have a mass explosion hazard

144. ______ Having a projection hazard but not a mass explosion hazard

145. ______ Having a minor explosion hazard confined mostly to package with no projection of fragments of appreciable size or range

146. ______ Very insensitive explosives having a mass explosion hazard but are so insensitive that there is very little probability of detonation under normal conditions of transport

147. ______ Having a mass explosion hazard

A. 1.1
B. 1.2
C. 1.3
D. 1.4
E. 1.5
F. 1.6

3

Match DOT Class 2 hazards with their division numbers. Write the correct letters in the blanks.

148. _______ Corrosive gases

149. _______ Nonflammable compressed gas

150. _______ Poisonous gases

151. _______ Flammable gas

A. 2.1
B. 2.2
C. 2.3
D. 2.4 (Canada only)

Match DOT classified hazardous materials with their division numbers. Write the correct letters in the blanks.

152. _______ Infectious substance

153. _______ Dangerous when wet material

154. _______ Corrosive material

155. _______ Flammable solid

156. _______ Spontaneously combustible material

157. _______ Combustible and flammable liquids

158. _______ Organic peroxide

159. _______ Radioactive material

160. _______ Miscellaneous hazardous material

161. _______ Poisonous material

162. _______ Oxidizer

A. 3
B. 4.1
C. 4.2
D. 4.3
E. 5.1
F. 5.2
G. 6.1
H. 6.2
I. 7
J. 8
K. 9

Match placard and label pictorial symbols with their hazard class names. Write the correct letters in the blanks.

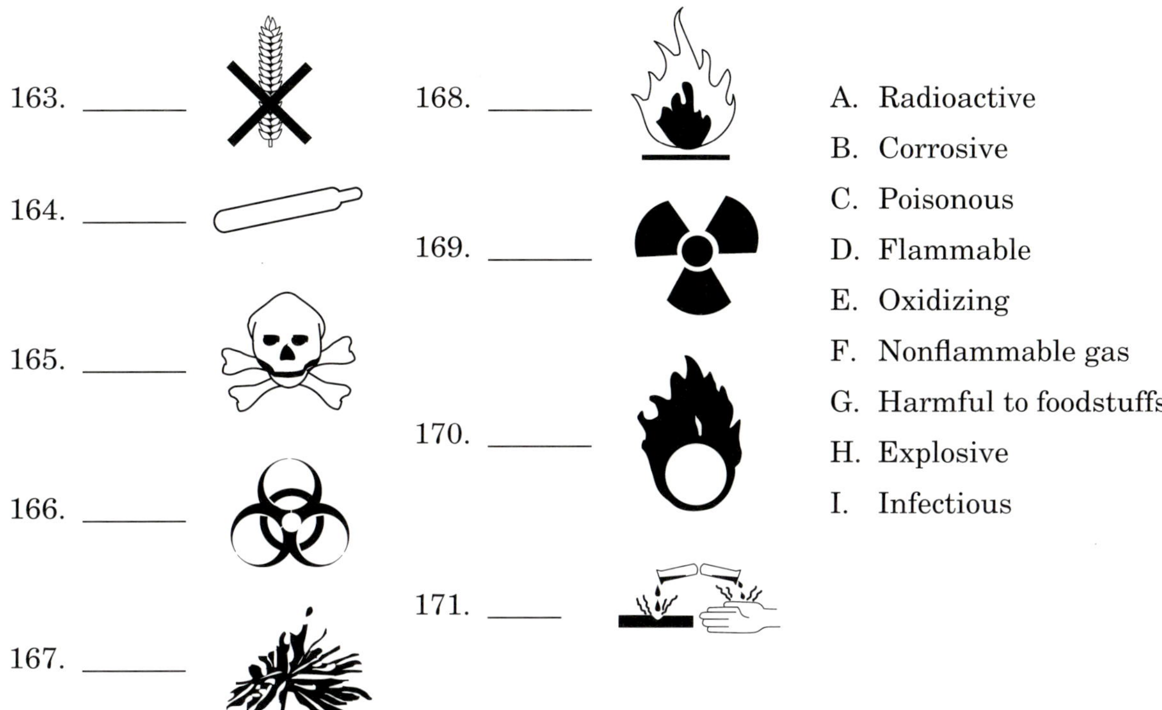

163. ______

164. ______

165. ______

166. ______

167. ______

168. ______

169. ______

170. ______

171. ______

A. Radioactive

B. Corrosive

C. Poisonous

D. Flammable

E. Oxidizing

F. Nonflammable gas

G. Harmful to foodstuffs

H. Explosive

I. Infectious

Match U.S. hazard placard background colors with their hazard classes. Write the correct letters in the blanks.

172. ______ Corrosives

173. ______ Water reactive materials

174. ______ Oxidizing substances

175. ______ Explosives

176. ______ Nonflammable gases

177. ______ Flammable and combustible liquids and gases

178. ______ Flammable solids

179. ______ Radioactive materials

180. ______ Poisons and infectious substances

A. Orange

B. Red

C. Green

D. Red & white vertical stripes

E. Red & white vertical stripes/blue top quadrant

F. Yellow

G. White

H. Yellow above white

I. White above black

3

Match U.S. haz mat warning label background colors with their hazard words. Write the correct letters in the blanks.

181. _______ Explosive; Blasting Agent

182. _______ Poison Gas

183. _______ Flammable Gas; Flammable Liquid

184. _______ Nonflammable Gas

185. _______ Oxygen; Oxidizer; Organic Peroxide

186. _______ Flammable Solid

187. _______ Dangerous When Wet

188. _______ Poison; Poison Gas

189. _______ Empty

190. _______ Biomedical Material

191. _______ Radioactive I

192. _______ Radioactive II; Radioactive III

193. _______ Corrosive

194. _______ Danger *[cargo aircraft only]*

195. _______ Magnetized Material

196. _______ Harmful: Stow Away from Foodstuffs

197. _______ Infectious Substance

A. White

B. White above black

C. Red

D. Red & white striped

E. Blue

F. Light blue rectangle

G. White rectangle with red & white right side

H. Orange

I. Orange square

J. Yellow

K. Yellow above white

L. Green

M. White square

Match NFPA 704 placards with their chemicals. Write the correct letters in the blanks. Consult NFPA 704 and NFPA 49 as necessary.

198. _______ Acetic acid

199. _______ Liquefied ammonia

200. _______ Acetylene

201. _______ Sodium peroxide

202. _______ Diethyl ether

203. _______ Ethene

204. _______ Vinyl chloride

205. _______ Hydrogen acid (hydrogen cyanide)

206. _______ Sulfuric acid

207. _______ Xylene

208. _______ Hydrochloric acid (hydrogen chloride)

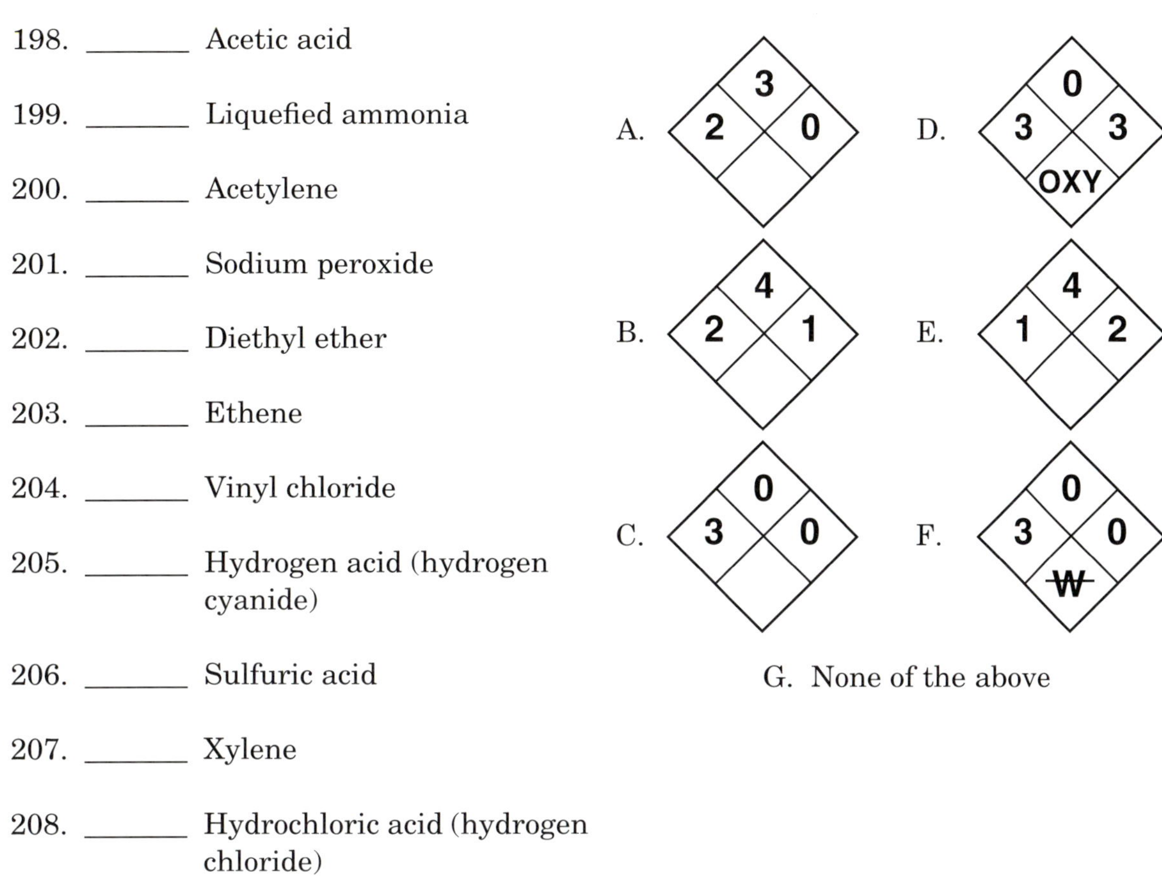

G. None of the above

Match with their probable contents types of highway vehicles used to transport hazardous materials. Write the correct letters in the blanks. (See matching column on next page.)

209. _______ Flammable liquids such as gasoline and alcohol; combustible liquids such as fuel oil; Division 6.1 poisons; liquid food products; vapor pressure under 3 psi (20 kPa)

210. _______ Various chemicals that may be flammable, corrosive, or poisonous; vapor pressure not to exceed 40 psi (280 kPa)

211. _______ Various types of hazardous materials in dry or slurry forms that can burn and release toxic products

3

212. _______ Acids; vapor pressure may range to 75 psi (517 kPa)

213. _______ Gases such as propane, butane, and anhydrous ammonia that have been compressed to a liquefied state

214. _______ Gases such as LOX, nitrogen, hydrogen, and carbon dioxide, that have been liquefied by temperature reduction

215. _______ Compressed gases such as air, argon, helium, hydrogen, nitrogen, oxygen, and refrigerants

216. _______ Liquid and solid materials — such as aluminum and sulfur — carried in their molten states

A. Low-pressure carrier (MC-307/DOT-407)

B. Cryogenic liquid carrier (MC-338)

C. Atmospheric pressure carrier (MC-306/DOT-406)

D. Dry bulk carrier

E. Elevated-temperature materials carrier

F. High-pressure carrier (MC-331)

G. Corrosive liquid carrier (MC-312/DOT-412)

H. Tube trailer

Match to their probable contents types of railcars used to transport hazardous materials. Write the correct letters in the blanks.

217. _______ Argon, nitrogen, hydrogen, oxygen

218. _______ Flammable and combustible liquids, flammable solids, oxidizers, Division 6.1 poisons, organic peroxides, molten solids, and corrosives

219. _______ Flammable and nonflammable liquefied gases, poisons, ethylene oxide, sodium metal, anhydrous hydrofluoric acid, motor fuel anti-knock compounds

A. Nonpressure tank railcar

B. Pressure tank railcar

C. Cryogenic-liquid tank railcar

3

Match U.S. military hazard symbols with their descriptions. Write the correct letters in the blanks.

220. _____ 

221. _____ 

222. _____ 

223. _____ 

224. _____ 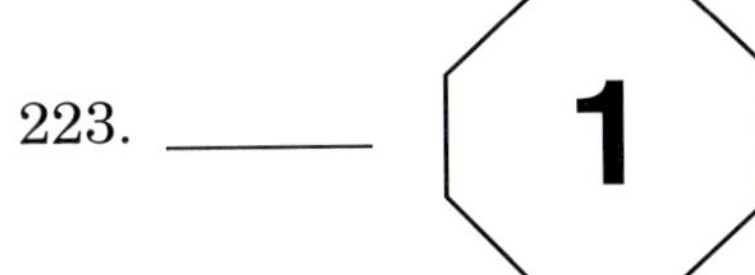

225. _____ 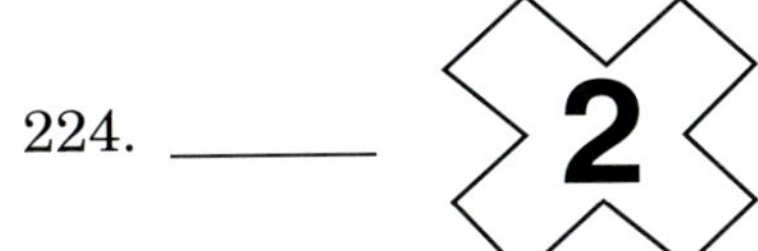

226. _____ 

A. Chemical hazard

B. Moderate fire hazard

C. Explosion with fragments

D. Mass detonation

E. Wear protective mask or breathing apparatus

F. Mass fire hazard

G. Apply no water

Match Canadian explosives classes with their symbols. Write the correct letters in the blanks.

227. _____ 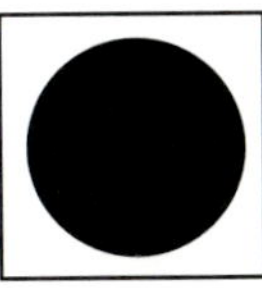

228. _____ 

229. _____ 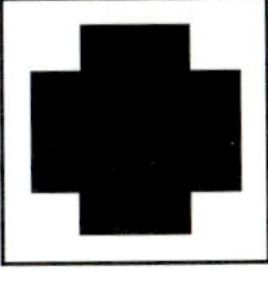

230. _____ 

231. _____ 

232. _____ 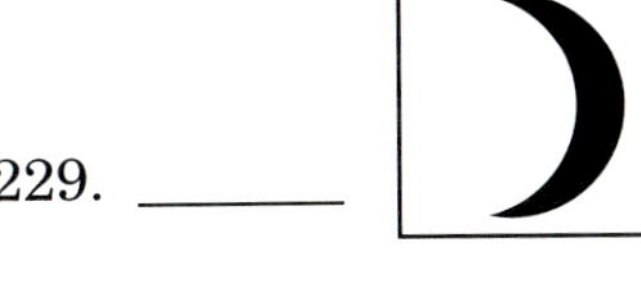

233. _____ 

234. _____ 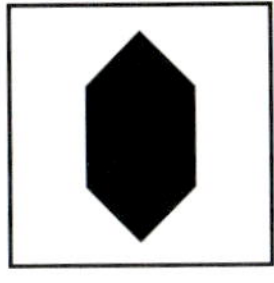

235. _____ 

A. Class 1

B. Class 2

C. Class 3

D. Class 4

E. Class 5

F. Class 6

G. Class 7

H. Class 8

I. MP

3

IDENTIFICATION

Identify the following acronyms and initials.

236. NRT ____

237. *ERG* ____

238. DOT ____

239. *IERG* ____

240. UN/NA ____

241. PIN ____

242. NRC ____

243. NACA ____

244. LPG ____

245. LNG ____

246. CGA ____

247. MSDS ____

248. NTP ____

249. IARC ____

250. CAS ____

251. HMTA ____

252. TDG ____

253. NRC ____

254. EPA ____

255. DOE ____

256. OSHA ____

257. ORM-D ____

3

258. LOX ____

259. TOFC ____

260. COFC ____

261. IM ____

262. PCP ____

263. PCB ____

Identify country codes found on intermodal containers.

Hint: Some countries use two different codes.

264. US _______________________________

277. SXX _______________________________

265. SGP _______________________________

278. RCX _______________________________

266. BM _______________________________

279. PIX _______________________________

267. PRC _______________________________

280. NZX _______________________________

268. PA _______________________________

281. LIB _______________________________

269. NLX _______________________________

282. JXX _______________________________

270. KR _______________________________

283. ILX _______________________________

271. IXX _______________________________

284. GB _______________________________

272. HKXX _______________________________

285. DKX _______________________________

273. FXX _______________________________

286. CHS _______________________________

274. DE _______________________________

287. JP _______________________________

275. BER _______________________________

288. FR _______________________________

276. PNM _______________________________

289. CH _______________________________

3

Identify fixed facility containers used to store hazardous materials.

290. _______________________________

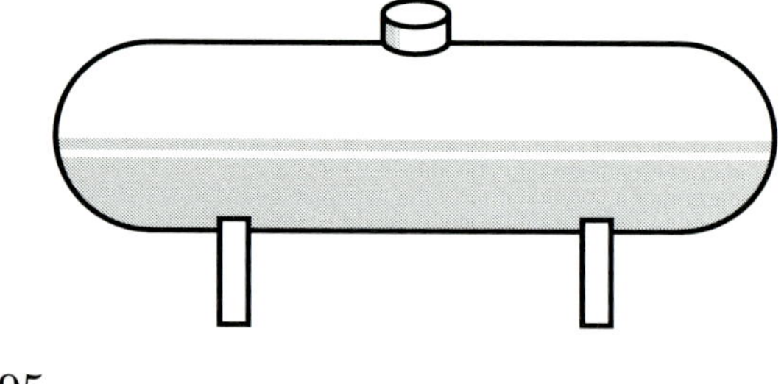

295. _______________________________

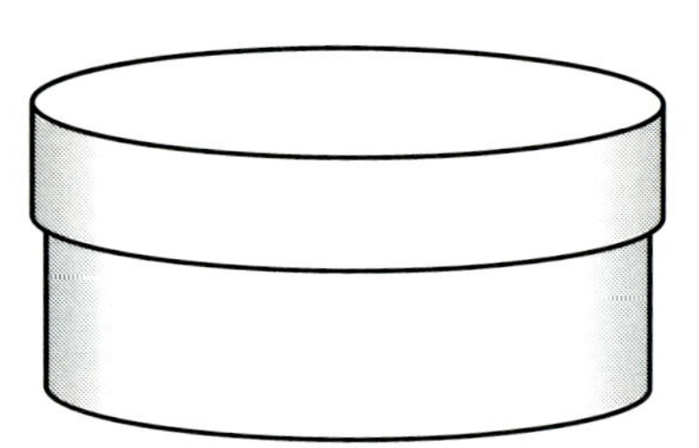

291. _______________________________

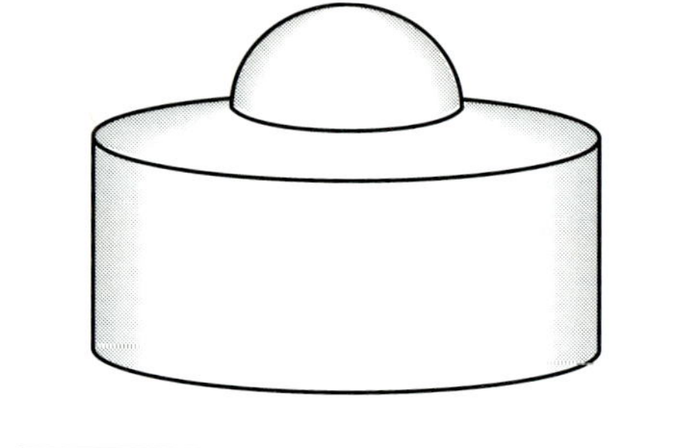

296. _______________________________

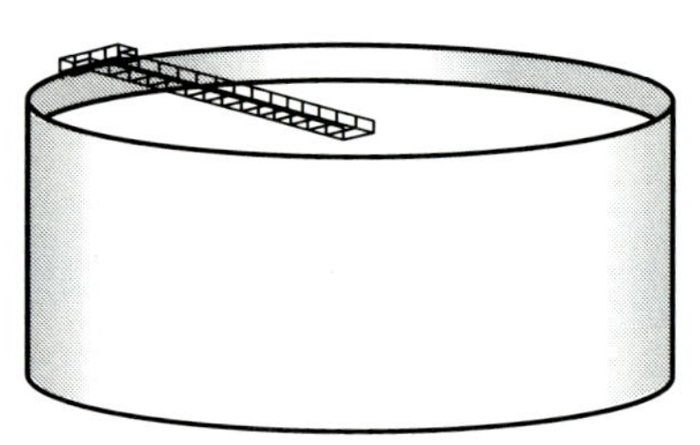

292. _______________________________

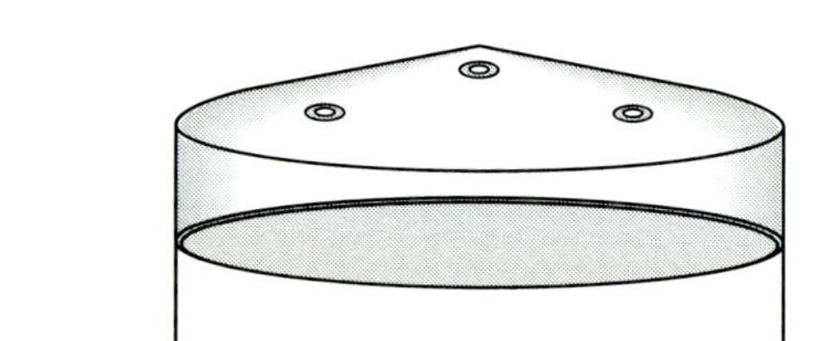

297. _______________________________

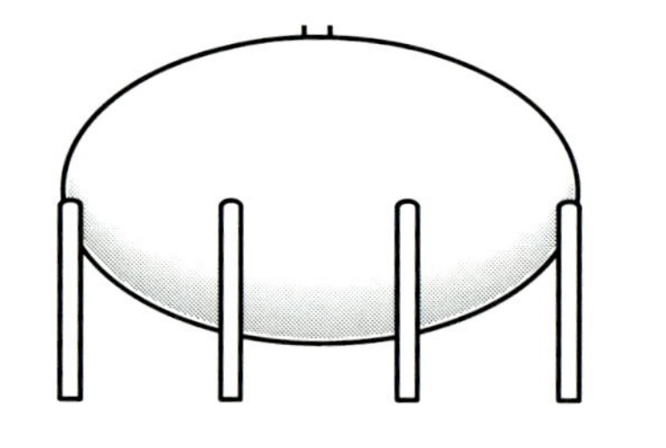

293. _______________________________

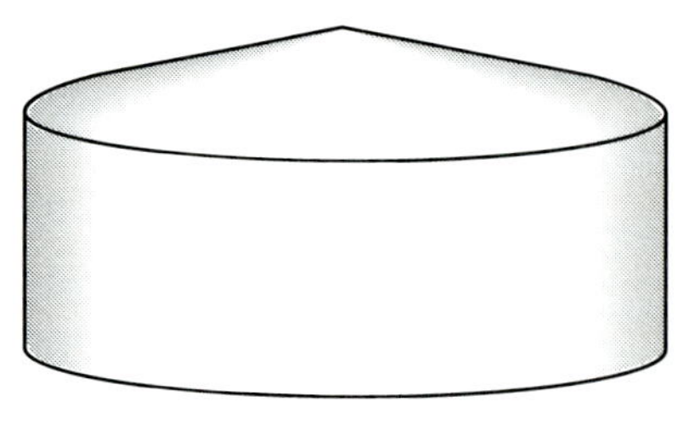

298. _______________________________

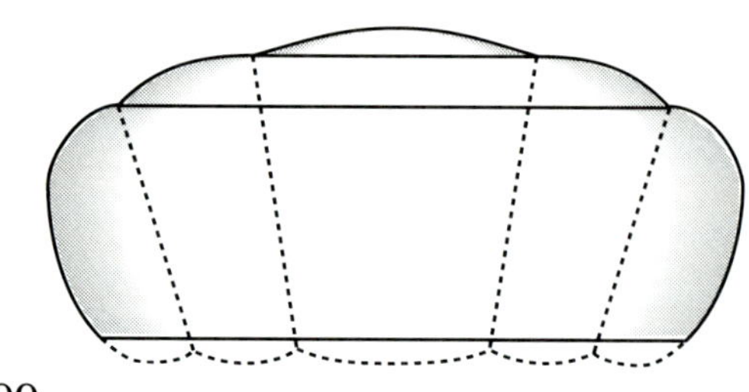

294. _______________________________

299. _______________________________

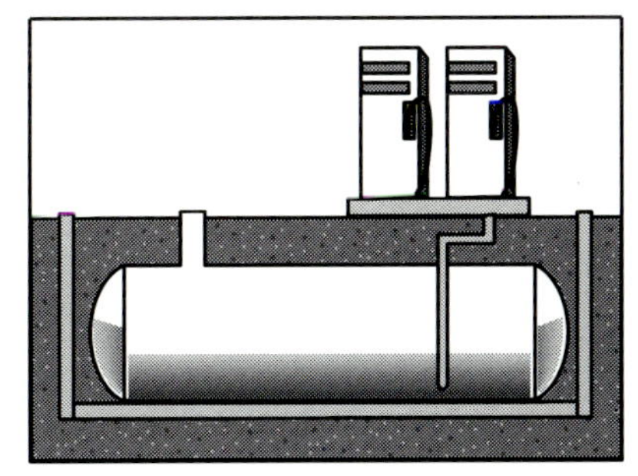

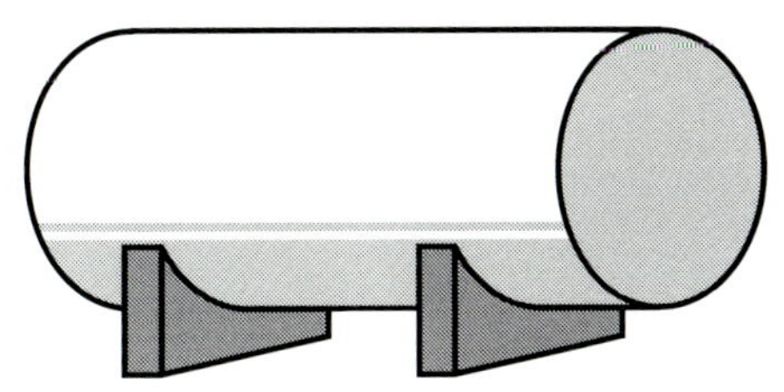

300. _________________________

301. _________________________

Identify the following items.

302. NFPA 704 ____

303. NFPA 30 ____

304. NFPA 49 ____

305. UN haz mat identification number _______________________________

306. Dedicated railcar _______________________________________

307. Bulk packaging ____

308. Assessment stop ____

309. CAS number ____

310. Christmas tree vent _____________________________________

Complete the following chart.

Shipping Paper Identification

Trans. Mode	Shipping Paper Name	Location of Papers	Party Responsible
Air	311. _________	312. _________	313. _________
Highway	314. _________	315. _________	316. _________
Rail	317. _________	318. _________	319. _________
Water	320. _________	321. _________	322. _________

3

Identify the following DOT terms and materials.

323. Mass explosion hazard *(per DOT Class 1)*

____

____

____

324. Flammable liquid *(per DOT Class 3)*

____

____

____

325. Combustible liquid *(per DOT Class 3)*

____

____

____

326. Oxidizer *(per DOT Class 5)*

____

____

____

327. Infectious substance *(per DOT Class 6)*

____

____

____

Identify hazardous materials cargo tank truck, trailer, and carrier outlines. Write the correct name below each illustration.

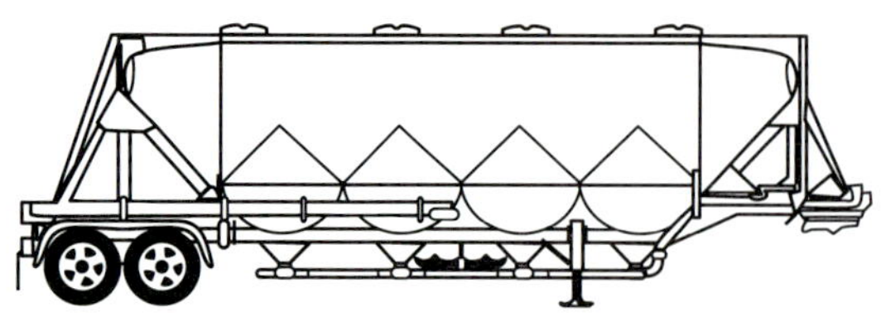

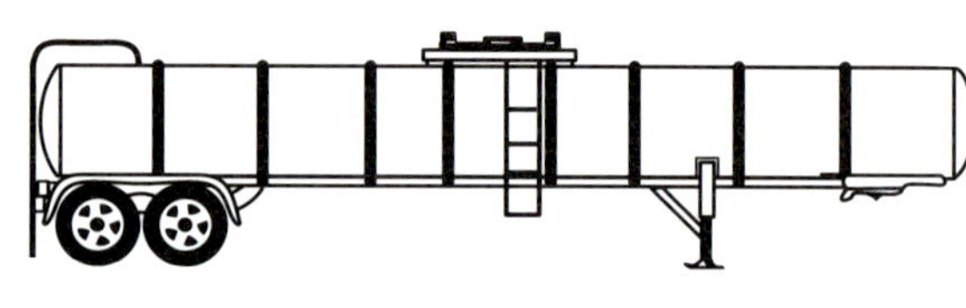

328. _______________________________   329. _______________________________

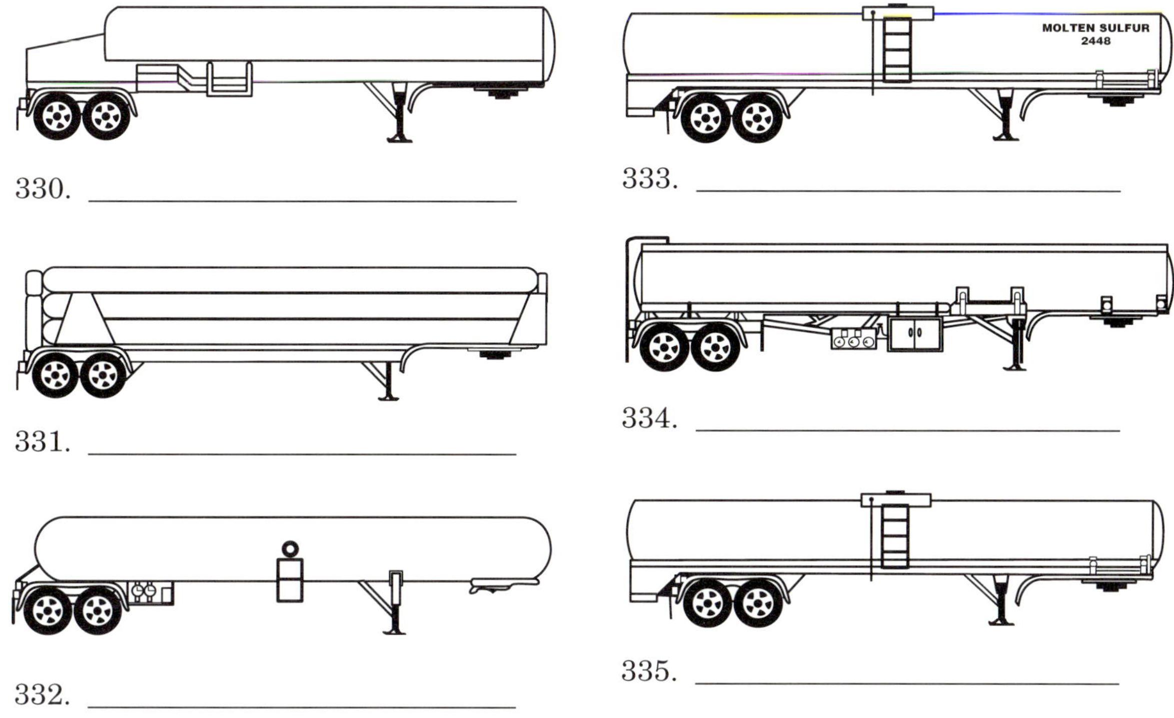

330. _______________________________

331. _______________________________

332. _______________________________

333. _______________________________

334. _______________________________

335. _______________________________

Identify haz mat tank railcar outlines. Write the correct name below each illustration.

336. _______________________________

338. _______________________________

337. _______________________________

3

Distinguish among identifying characteristics of pressure (P), nonpressure (NP), cryogenic (CY), and dedicated (DR) railcars. Write the correct abbreviation before each characteristic.

339. _______ Relief valve for overpressure protection

340. _______ No bottom unloading piping under the car

341. _______ Visible fittings/expansion dome

342. _______ Manufacturer's name and logo largest print on railcar

343. _______ Safety vent for dumping contents at tank test pressure

344. _______ Multicompartmented with loading and unloading fittings for each compartment

345. _______ Protective housing around manhole, valves, gaging rod, and sampling well

346. _______ White with horizontal red stripe and two vertical red stripes at each end

347. _______ Protective black band around car under dome

348. _______ Large, insulated tank

349. _______ Generally no plumbing underneath

350. _______ Smaller than most general service railcars

351. _______ Ends of insulated/jacketed railcars less round than ends of thermally protected or single-shell railcars

352. _______ Tanks sometimes enclosed in a boxcar

353. _______ May be a distinctive color determined by the owner and not subject to regulation

Identify intermodal tank containers. Write the correct names in the blanks.

354. ____

355. ____

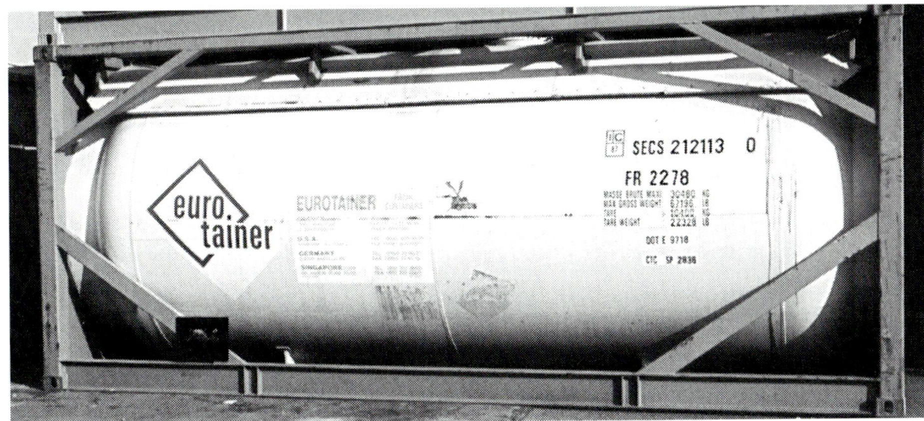

356. ____

3

Identify the following Canadian military class marking system for explosives.

357. Class 1

358. Class 2

359. Class 3

360. Class 4

361. Class 5

362. Class 6

363. Class 7

364. Class 8

365. Class MP

Using the DOT *Emergency Response Guidebook*, identify the correct Guide number and identification number or hazardous material.

Hazardous Material	ID No.	Guide No.
366. _______________________	1618	_______
367. _______________________	3021	_______
368. Enamel	_______	_______
369. _______________________	1203	_______
370. Sodium nitrate	_______	_______
371. Aviation fuel	_______	_______
372. _______________________	1693	_______
373. _______________________	1299	_______
374. Ammonium nitrate fertilizer	_______	_______
375. _______________________	2918	_______

LISTING

376. List the ten pieces of information required on shipping papers.

   A. ____

   B. ____

   C. ____

   D. ____

   E. ____

   F. ____

   G. ____

   H. ____

   I. ____

   J. ____

377. List at least one *specific* common hazardous material for each of the following U.S. DOT hazard classes.

   A. 1.1 ___________________   F. 1.6 ___________________

   B. 1.2 ___________________   G. 2.1 ___________________

   C. 1.3 ___________________   H. 2.2 ___________________

   D. 1.4 ___________________   I. 2.3 ___________________

   E. 1.5 ___________________   J. 3 ___________________

3

K. 4.1 _______________________   R. 7 _______________________

L. 4.2 _______________________   S. 8 _______________________

M. 4.3 _______________________   T. 9.1 _______________________

N. 5.1 _______________________   U. 9.2 _______________________

O. 5.2 _______________________   V. 9.3 _______________________

P. 6.1 _______________________   W. ORM-D _______________________

Q. 6.2 _______________________

378. List four informal methods of identifying a hazardous material.

A. ____

B. ____

C. ____

D. ____

379. List six questions that should be asked by officials at the scene who receive verbal reports of haz mat involvement.

A. ____

____

B. ____

____

C. ____

____

D. ____

____

E. ____

____

F. ____

____

380. List five common locations that are highly likely to use and store hazardous materials.

A. ____

B. ____

C. ____

D. ____

E. ____

381. List three places where haz mat accidents are likely to occur for *each* of the following transportation modes

    A. Highways

    B. Railways

    C. Water

    D. Air

    E. Pipeline

382. List the purposes of remote assessment stops.

    A.

    B.

    C.

    D.

    E.

3

3

383. List four examples to illustrate visual and sensory evidence of physical actions and chemical reactions that indicate the presence of hazardous materials.

A. Physical actions _______________________________________

____

____

____

B. Chemical reactions _______________________________________

____

____

____

384. List the most common formal sources for verifying information obtained from a survey of a haz mat incident.

A. _______________________________________

B. _______________________________________

C. _______________________________________

D. _______________________________________

E. _______________________________________

385. List the information that a first responder should provide when contacting CHEMTREC/CANUTEC.

A. _______________________________________

B. _______________________________________

C. _______________________________________

D. _______________________________________

E. _______________________________________

F. _______________________________________

G. _______________________________________

H. _______________________________________

I. _______________________________________

386. List limitations to the CHEMTREC/CANUTEC emergency information centers.

A. _______________________________________

____

B. _______________________________________

____

3

    C. ____

       ____

    D. ____

       ____

387. List four associations other than CHEMTREC/CANUTEC that may provide technical assistance to the first responder.

    A. ____

    B. ____

    C. ____

    D. ____

388. List the toll-free emergency number for CHEMTREC or the collect emergency telephone number for CANUTEC — whichever is applicable for your location.

    A. CHEMTREC _______________________________________

    B. CANUTEC _______________________________________

389. List the eight areas of information that an MSDS must contain.

    A. Section I _______________________________________

    B. Section II _______________________________________

    C. Section III _______________________________________

    D. Section IV _______________________________________

    E. Section V _______________________________________

    F. Section VI _______________________________________

    G. Section VII _______________________________________

    H. Section VIII _______________________________________

390. List three pieces of information that would be found in each MSDS section listed in Question 389.

    Section I

    A. ____

    B. ____

    C. ____

3

Section II

A. ____

B. ____

C. ____

Section III

A. ____

B. ____

C. ____

Section IV

A. ____

B. ____

C. ____

Section V

A. ____

B. ____

C. ____

Section VI

A. ____

B. ____

C. ____

Section VII

A. ____

B. ____

C. ____

Section VIII

A. ____

B. ____

C. ____

391. List Canada's three Class 9 divisions.

A. ____

B. ____

C. ____

392. List the four methods that shippers and carriers use to meet DOT regulations that require them to "communicate" the hazards of their cargoes.

    A. ____

    B. ____

    C. ____

    D. ____

393. List descriptive information that must appear on shipping papers for hazardous materials.

    A. ____

    B. ____

    C. ____

    D. ____

394. List two examples of specialized intermodal tank containers.

    A. ____

    B. ____

395. List the five criteria upon which informal identification of hazardous materials in railcars can be based.

    A. ____

    B. ____

    C. ____

    D. ____

    E. ____

396. List five types of nonbulk packaging.

    A. ____

    B. ____

    C. ____

    D. ____

    E. ____

397. List the three types of safety relief devices that may be found on compressed-gas cylinders.

    A. ____

    B. ____

    C. ____

3

398. List five pieces of information (in addition to the mandated EPA signal word) that may be found on pesticide labels.

A. ____

B. ____

C. ____

D. ____

E. ____

399. List the three most common types of monitoring instruments available to first responders.

A. ____

B. ____

C. ____

LABELING

400. Label the parts of the NFPA 704 marking below. Write the correct names in the blanks corresponding to the lettered parts.

A. _______________________________________

B. _______________________________________

C. _______________________________________

D. _______________________________________

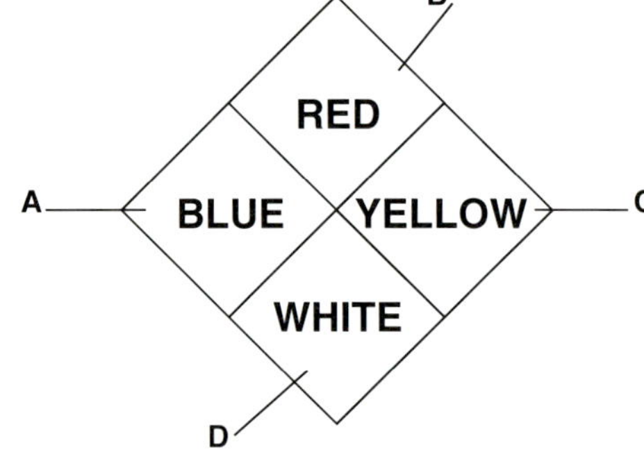

401. Label the parts of the shipping label below. Write the correct names in the blanks corresponding to the lettered parts.

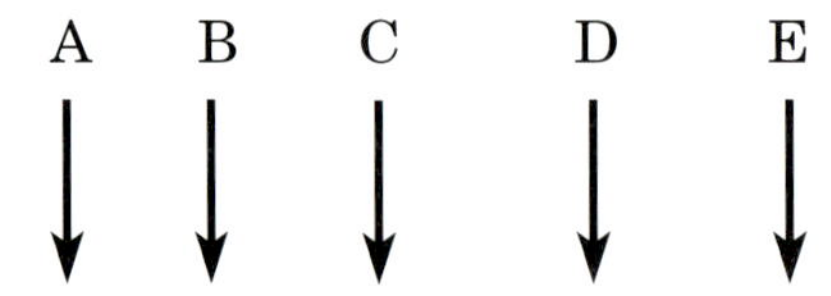

A. _______________________________   D. _______________________________

B. _______________________________   E. _______________________________

C. _______________________________

3

402. Label the hazard recognition features of the typical haz mat placard below. Write the correct names in the blanks corresponding to the lettered parts.

A. _______________________

B. _______________________

C. _______________________

D. _______________________

403. Label/interpret the intermodal tank markings below. Write the correct names in the blanks corresponding to the lettered parts.

A. _______________________

B. _______________________

C. _______________________

D. _______________________

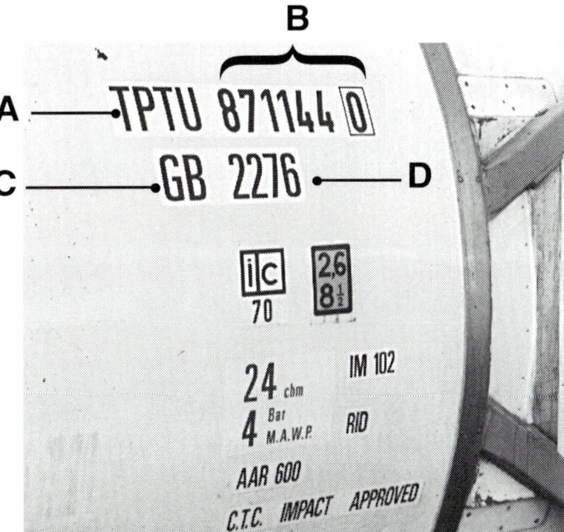

404. Label information on the pipeline marker below. Write the correct names in the blanks corresponding to the lettered parts.

A. _______________________

B. _______________________

C. _______________________

D. _______________________

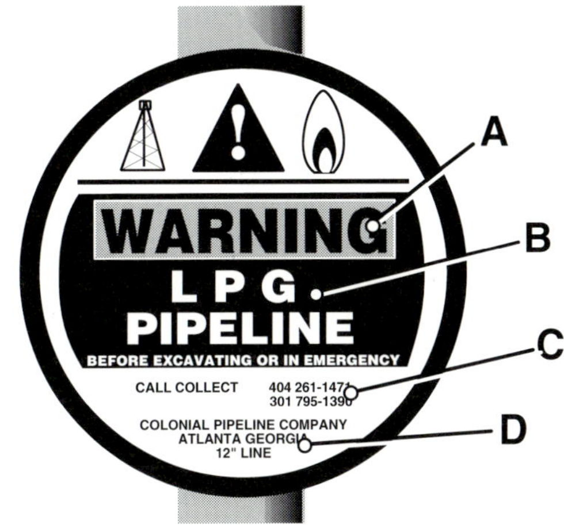

3

Briefly answer each question in your own words.

405. What three steps may first responders take to lay the groundwork at a haz mat incident and reduce the number of on-site decisions?

A. ____

B. ____

C. ____

406. What important information does haz mat pre-incident planning seek to identify?

A. ____

____

B. ____

____

C. ____

____

D. ____

____

407. What is the first responder's primary resource for obtaining information on pre-incident planning?

____

____

408. Why must the first responder be wary of using informal methods of identification in highly probable haz mat use and storage locations?

____

____

____

____

409. Specifically describe each of the following symptoms of chemical exposure to a hazardous material.

A. Changes in respiration____

____

B. Changes in consciousness _______________________________________

____

C. Abdominal distress ____

____

D. Change in activity level ____

____

E. Visual disturbances ____

____

F. Skin changes ____

____

G. Changes in excretion or thirst ______________________________________

____

H. Pain ____

____

410. Contrast the *IERG* placarding/labeling system with the *ERG*'s system.

A. *IERG* ____

____

B. *ERG* ____

____

411. Describe the three general types of information provided by the NFPA 704 system.

____

____

____

____

____

____

412. What is the scope of the first responder's responsibility when determining the presence of hazardous materials through recognition of container types found at fixed facilities?

____

____

____

413. Explain the purpose of DOT's marking regulations.

____

____

____

____

3

414. Explain the differences among haz mat container markings, labels, and placards.

A. Markings ____

____

B. Labels ____

____

C. Placards ____

____

415. How does the first responder determine what material is being transported in a dedicated railcar?

____

____

____

____

416. How are general service tank railcars distinguished from pressure railcars?

____

417. How may tank railcars that carry corrosives be distinguished from other types of general service cars?

____

____

418. Provide the capacities that a shipment must have before it is considered bulk packaging.

A. Maximum capacity (liquid) = ____

____

B. Maximum net mass (solid) = ____

____

C. Maximum capacity (in gallons/liters) as a receptacle for a solid = __________

____

D. Liquid capacity (in pounds/kilograms) as a receptacle for a gas = __________

____

419. Explain why a first responder must exercise extreme caution when approaching any military vehicle involved in an accident or fire.

____

____

____

____

420. Distinguish among the following EPA pesticide label signal words.

A. DANGER/POISON ____

B. WARNING ____

C. CAUTION ____

Chapter 4

Photo Courtesy of Scott D. Christiansen, Minot, N.D..

HAZ MAT

Hazard And Risk Assessment

Hazard And Risk Assessment | 4

Define each of the following terms.

1. Ballistic

2. Breach

3. Deflagration

4. Divert

5. Engulf

6. Harm

7. Impingement

8. Mitigation

4

9. Polymerization

____

____

10. Strategy

____

____

11. Stress

____

____

TRUE/FALSE

Mark each of the following statements true (T) or false (F). Correct each false statement.

12. ☐ T ☐ F First responders usually identify and complete a primary objective for each specific emergency.

____

____

13. ☐ T ☐ F The hazard that most affects all areas of response is the size and extent of the incident.

____

____

14. ☐ T ☐ F The duration of a detonation can be measured in hundredths or thousandths of a second.

____

____

15. ☐ T ☐ F Incident commanders should put objectives in the form of a statement of what they hope to accomplish.

____

____

16. ☐ T ☐ F Usually there is only one correct way to achieve an objective.

____

____

17. ☐ T ☐ F Immediate-concern tasks require no specialized equipment.

    ____

    ____

18. ☐ T ☐ F Detonation is best defined as the immediate release of chemical or mechanical energy caused by runaway cracks.

    ____

    ____

19. ☐ T ☐ F First responders must always be aware that the two things that will endanger them during a release are energy and matter.

    ____

    ____

MATCHING

Match container/attachment damage to the physical force that could cause it. Write the correct letters in the blanks.

20. ________ Changes the shape of the container

21. ________ Reduces thickness of container

22. ________ Unfastens or damages valves and piping or penetrates container wall

A. Cracking or gouging force

B. Crushing force

C. Abrading or scoring force

Match the following actions with their strategic objectives. Write the correct letters in the blanks.

23. ________ Confining hazard to given area

24. ________ Allowing incident to run its own course

25. ________ Controlling the incident

A. Defensive strategy

B. Offensive strategy

C. Nonintervention strategy

IDENTIFICATION

Identify the following items.

26. Footprint ____

27. GEBMO ____

28. Immediate concern tasks ____

4

29. Primary objective ____

30. Strategic objective ____

Provide the requested information.

31. Identify the analyses processes dictated by the DECIDE acronym.

    A. **D** ____

    B. **E** ____

    C. **C** ____

    D. **I** ____

    E. **D** ____

    F. **E** ____

32. Identify the systematic decision-making approach dictated by the IFSTA acronym.

    A. **I** ____

    B. **F** ____

    C. **S** ____

    D. **T** ____

    E. **A** ____

33. Identify the outlines of the dispersing hazardous materials in the following illustrations. Write the correct names beneath the illustrations.

    A. ____

B. ____

C. ____

D. ____

4

E. ____

F. ____

LISTING

34. List five examples of immediate concern tasks.

    A. ____

    B. ____

    C. ____

    D. ____

    E. ____

35. List three examples of primary objectives.

    A. ____

    B. ____

    C. ____

36. List four factors that determine how and when a primary objective is achieved.

    A. ____

    B. ____

C. ____

D. ____

37. List the criteria upon which strategic objectives must be based.

    A. ____

    B. ____

    C. ____

       ____

38. List two strategic activities that cannot be performed until the first responder arrives at the scene and assesses the situation.

    A. ____

    B. ____

39. List seven questions that enable the incident commander to take the first step in strategic decision making: identification of the problem.

    A. ____

    B. ____

    C. ____

    D. ____

    E. ____

    F. ____

    G. ____

40. List the questions that the first responder should ask when assessing a haz mat situation to identify the appropriate response.

    A. ____

    B. ____

    C. ____

    D. ____

41. List the six conditions and associated behaviors of the GEBMO system for developing a strategy for limiting the effects of a haz mat incident.

    A. ____

    B. ____

    C. ____

    D. ____

    E. ____

    F. ____

4

4

42. List the three most common classes of container stressors.

A. ____

B. ____

C. ____

43. List (from fastest to least rapid) the four ways in which containment systems can release their contents.

A. ___________________________   C. ___________________________

B. ___________________________   D. ___________________________

44. List the three factors that determine the degree of harm to a haz mat exposure.

A. ____

B. ____

C. ____

SHORT ANSWER

Briefly answer each question in your own words.

45. Explain how — in some cases — the first responder is able to control the direction a haz mat incident is going to take.

____

____

____

____

46. What are the incident commander's primary concerns regarding strategic objectives?

____

____

____

47. In the IFSTA decision-making process, what are the three desired outcomes that the first responder hopes to achieve when selecting alternatives?

A. ____

B. ____

C. ____

48. Distinguish among the four ways in which containment systems can release their contents.

    A. ____

    ____

    ____

    ____

    B. ____

    ____

    ____

    ____

    C. ____

    ____

    ____

    ____

    D. ____

    ____

    ____

    ____

49. Provide one *specific* example to illustrate each of the following types of breaches.

    A. Disintegration ____

    B. Runaway cracking ____

    C. Attachments (closures) opening up ____

    D. Puncture ____

    E. Split or tear ____

50. Provide one *specific* example for each of the following contact durations.

    A. Immediate ____

    B. Short term ____

    C. Medium term ____

    D. Long term ____

Chapter 5

Photo Courtesy of Scott D. Christiansen, Minot, N.D..

Personal Protective Equipment

Personal Protective Equipment

5

Define each of the following terms.

1. Cryogenic

2. Catalyst

3. Dedicated (as in a *dedicated* area)

4. Encapsulating

5. Leach

6. Nullify

7. Permeate

8. Proximity

5

9. Sorbent

____

____

10. Sorption

____

____

11. Untethered

____

____

Mark each of the following statements true (T) or false (F). Correct each false statement.

12. ☐ T ☐ F High-temperature protective clothing offers adequate protection against chemical hazards.

____

____

13. ☐ T ☐ F Level A protective equipment consists of ordinary work clothes and uniforms.

____

____

14. ☐ T ☐ F Level D protection is not adequate for first responders.

____

____

15. ☐ T ☐ F Only Level A protective equipment includes respiratory protection and protects against all hazards.

____

____

16. ☐ T ☐ F Turnout clothing should always be cleaned in a dedicated area away from other clothing.

____

____

5

17. ☐ T ☐ F   The materials used in chemical-protective clothing offer good protection against some chemicals but not against all chemicals.

18. ☐ T ☐ F   Limited-use chemical-protective clothing should be decontaminated and disposed of after use.

19. ☐ T ☐ F   Reusable chemical-protective clothing can retain some chemicals even after decontamination.

20. ☐ T ☐ F   Vapor-protective suits are primarily used as part of a Level B protective ensemble.

21. ☐ T ☐ F   Support-function protective garments are worn by personnel working inside the hot zone.

22. ☐ T ☐ F   Support-function suits may be encapsulating and worn with protective breathing equipment.

23. ☐ T ☐ F   Chemical-protective clothing should not be used in conjunction with any other protective equipment required by the situation.

24. ☐ T ☐ F   Each of the three types of high-temperature suits has a specific use and is not interchangeable.

5

25. ☐ T   ☐ F   Closed-circuit SCBA are the most commonly used protective breathing apparatus in the fire service.

____

____

26. ☐ T   ☐ F   The air supply in an open-circuit SCBA is pure oxygen.

____

____

27. ☐ T   ☐ F   Most SCBA allow a firefighter to perform at least 30 to 60 minutes of heavy work.

____

____

28. ☐ T   ☐ F   NFPA and ANSI standards require that only demand-type breathing apparatus be used in the fire service.

____

____

29. ☐ T   ☐ F   Airline equipment is most commonly used by special haz mat cleanup companies.

____

____

30. ☐ T   ☐ F   The shape and contour of the face affect the wearer's ability to get a good facepiece-to-face seal.

____

____

31. ☐ T   ☐ F   Air-purifying respirators can be worn in IDLH or oxygen-deficient atmospheres.

____

____

32. ☐ T   ☐ F   An excited person uses more SCBA air than a calm person.

____

____

33. ☐ T   ☐ F   SCBA must be cleaned and sanitized after each use.

____

____

MULTIPLE CHOICE

Circle the letter before the most appropriate response.

34. Which of the following is NOT a type of chemical-protective clothing?
    A. Vapor-protective suits
    B. Liquid-splash protective suits
    C. Antiabsorption protective suits
    D. Support-function protective garments

35. Which of the following statements is false?
    A. Chemical-protective clothing is available in disposable and reusable versions.
    B. The rubber or neoprene in boots, gloves, and SCBA masks in structural fire fighting clothing can become permeated by chemicals and render them unsafe for use.
    C. The manufacturer of a particular chemical-protective suit must provide a list of chemicals with which the suit is compatible.
    D. Limited-use chemical-protective clothing can be decontaminated and reused if it is not damaged.

36. Which type of protective breathing equipment is used most extensively by haz mat first responders?
    A. Open-circuit SCBA
    B. Open-circuit airline
    C. Closed-circuit SCBA
    D. Air-purifying respirator

37. What type of protective breathing equipment recycles exhaled air for "rebreathing"?
    A. Open-circuit SCBA
    B. Closed-circuit SCBA
    C. Open-circuit airline
    D. Air-purifying respirator

38. What kind of breathing air does an air-purifying respirator use?
    A. Ambient air
    B. Compressed air
    C. Pure oxygen
    D. Recycled compressed air

39. Which of the following is NOT an example of an air-purifying respirator?
    A. Vapor- and gas-removing respirator
    B. Particulate-filtering respirator
    C. Powered air-purifying respirator
    D. Vapor- and particulate-removing respirator

5

MATCHING

Match types of high-temperature clothing with their uses. Write the correct letters in the blanks.

40. _______ Permits firefighters to work in environments that contain high levels of radiated heat

41. _______ Permits close approach to fires, enabling rescue, fire suppression, and property conservation activities

42. _______ Permits a person to work in total flame environments for short periods of time

A. Fire entry suit
B. Proximity suit
C. Approach suit

IDENTIFICATION

Identify the following abbreviations and acronyms.

43. NIOSH ____

44. USCG ____

45. EPA ____

46. MSHA ____

47. *ERG* ____

48. *IERG* ____

49. NFPA 49 ____

50. NFPA 1991 ____

51. NFPA 1992 ____

52. NFPA 1993 ____

53. NFPA 472 ____

54. OSHA 29 CFR 1910.134 ____

____

Distinguish among characteristics/uses of EPA protective equipment classifications. Write Level A, B, C, or D in the blank before the appropriate use or characteristic.

5

55. _______ Emergency response personnel should not use this level protective equipment unless the specific material is known and can be measured

56. _______ Protects against splashes from specified hazardous chemicals

57. _______ Ordinary work clothes and uniforms

58. _______ Encapsulating suit envelops both wearer and SCBA

59. _______ Includes any of various types of air-purifying respirators

60. _______ Wrists, ankles, facepiece and hood, and waist are secured to prevent entry of splashed liquid

61. _______ Same type of garment as for Level B but allows for the use of respiratory protective equipment other than SCBA

62. _______ Provides inadequate protection for first responders

63. _______ May require specific types of boots and gloves, which may or may not be attached to the garments

64. _______ Is required when working directly with liquids, vapors, or gases that pose a severe threat of injury from any contact

LISTING

65. List the articles of clothing that comprise structural fire fighting *full protective clothing*.

    A. ___________________________   D. ___________________________

    B. ___________________________   E. ___________________________

    C. ___________________________   F. ___________________________

66. List three limitations of structural fire fighting clothing.

    A. ____

    ____

    B. ____

    ____

    C. ____

    ____

5

67. List two limitations to general chemical-protective clothing.

    A. ____

    B. ____

68. List the three classes of vapor- and gas-removing respirators.

    A. ____

    B. ____

    C. ____

69. List five conditions that place first responders at risk when wearing SCBA.

    A. ____

    B. ____

    C. ____

    D. ____

    E. ____

70. List five limitations of protective breathing equipment.

    A. ____

    B. ____

    C. ____

    D. ____

    E. ____

71. List five limitations of protective breathing equipment air supply.

    A. ____

    B. ____

    C. ____

    D. ____

    E. ____

72. Use the *ERG* to list the protective clothing recommended for first responders at incidents involving the following hazardous materials.

    A. Chlordane

    ____

    ____

    ____

5

B. Flammable solid (3178)

C. Uranium nitrate hexahydrate solution

D. Molten aluminum

E. Radioactive material (2974)

F. Fissile uranium hexafluoride

G. Refrigerated liquid hydrogen

H. Anhydrous ammonia

I. Asbestos

5

73. Use the *ERG* to list the Guide number and health hazards associated with inadequate personal protection at incidents involving the following hazardous materials.

A. Acrolein (uninhibited)

- Guide number: _______________________________

- Health hazards: _______________________________

____

____

____

____

B. Vinyl butyl ether

- Guide number: _______________________________

- Health hazards: _______________________________

____

____

____

____

C. Petroleum naptha

- Guide number: _______________________________

- Health hazards: _______________________________

____

____

____

____

D. Methyl chloride

- Guide number: _______________________________

- Health hazards: _______________________________

____

____

____

____

E. Hydrochloric acid solution

- Guide number: ___________________________

- Health hazards: ____

____

____

____

____

F. Refrigerated (cryogenic) liquid helium

- Guide number: ___________________________

- Health hazards: ____

____

____

____

____

G. Asbestos

- Guide number: ___________________________

- Health hazards: ____

____

____

____

____

H. LOX

- Guide number: ___________________________

- Health hazards: ____

____

____

____

____

5

Briefly answer each question in your own words.

74. Contrast the intended uses of the open-circuit airline egress cylinder with the small, closed-circuit cylinder.

    A. Egress cylinder

    B. Closed-circuit cylinder

75. Explain each of the physical, medical, and mental factors that affect the first responder's ability to use SCBA effectively.

    A. Physical condition

    B. Agility

    C. Facial features

    D. Neurological functioning

    E. Muscular/skeletal condition

5

F. Cardiovascular conditioning

G. Respiratory functioning

H. Training in equipment use

I. Self-confidence

J. Emotional stability

Chapter 6

Photo Courtesy of Scott D. Christiansen, Minot, N.D..

HAZ MAT

Command, Safety, And Scene Control

Command, Safety, And Scene Control | 6

Define the following terms.

1. Estuary

2. Utilidor

Mark each of the following statements true (T) or false (F). Correct each false statement.

3. ☐ T ☐ F There is no legislation in Canada that is comparable to SARA Title III.

4. ☐ T ☐ F Canadian EMOs cover essentially the same information as U.S. LERPs.

5. ☐ T ☐ F First responders should carry a copy of the LERP to each response.

6. ☐ T ☐ F The telephone is the most commonly used medium for reporting an emergency.

6

7. ☐ T ☐ F The dispatcher should be familiar with the department's SOPs, the LERP, and any special procedures for making haz mat incident notifications and information requests.

8. ☐ T ☐ F Dispatchers should not be included in responder training sessions or exercises.

9. ☐ T ☐ F Internal communication begins when the dispatcher receives the report of a haz mat incident.

10. ☐ T ☐ F Dispatchers should edit all information they receive.

11. ☐ T ☐ F If possible, all units operating at a haz mat incident should be switched to a separate radio frequency than those radio frequencies used for normal daily operations.

12. ☐ T ☐ F Sometimes the dispatcher must perform the function of technical advisor to a haz mat incident.

13. ☐ T ☐ F Once the incident action plan is formulated, the first responder at the operational level is expected to participate fully in the implementation of the plan.

14. ☐ T ☐ F The first person on the scene assumes and maintains command of the incident, even though a higher ranking individual may arrive at the scene later.

6

15. ☐ T ☐ F   The incident commander does not have to actually perform or supervise each of the functions for which he or she is responsible.

16. ☐ T ☐ F   The safety of the first responders is the uppermost consideration in selecting a mode of operation.

17. ☐ T ☐ F   A Level III incident is the least serious and the easiest to handle.

18. ☐ T ☐ F   If the material is on fire or has been leaking for longer than 30 minutes, the *Table of Initial Isolation and Protective Action Distances* in the *ERG* does not apply.

19. ☐ T ☐ F   The Canadian *IERG* does not contain initial evacuation distances.

20. ☐ T ☐ F   The smallest isolation distance given in the *ERG* for any chemical is 250 feet.

21. ☐ T ☐ F   Even after people have been evacuated and moved the *ERG* recommended distances, they are not completely safe from harm.

22. ☐ T ☐ F   Vehicles are more effective than buildings for protection-in-place.

23. ☐ T ☐ F   Control zones are not static and can be adjusted as the incident changes.

6

24. ☐ T ☐ F   It is considered unsafe for workers to enter the warm zone without special protective clothing.

____

____

25. ☐ T ☐ F   Workers in the cold zone are not required to wear personal protective clothing.

____

____

26. ☐ T ☐ F   The command post must be located where the incident commander can observe the scene.

____

____

27. ☐ T ☐ F   Responders do not need to protect themselves when transporting victims to the triage/treatment area because the victims have already been decontaminated.

____

____

MULTIPLE CHOICE

Circle the letter before the most appropriate response.

28. When is a formal plan of action decided upon and implemented?
    A. During pre-incident planning
    B. En route
    C. At the scene
    D. On receipt of all information from reporting individual

29. On what color Guide page in the *IERG* is evacuation information found?
    A. Green
    B. Orange
    C. Blue
    D. Yellow

30. According to the *ERG Table of Initial Isolation and Protective Action Distances*, what constitutes a small spill?
    A. Spill area equal to or smaller than 55 feet in diameter
    B. Spill area equal to or smaller than 60 feet in diameter
    C. Spill from a single package equal to or smaller than 110 gallons (two 55-gallon drums)
    D. Spill from a single small package (up to 55-gallon drum), small cylinder, or a small leak from a large package

31. According to the *ERG Table of Initial Isolation and Protective Action Distances*, what constitutes a large spill?
    A. Spill from a large package or multiple spills from many small packages
    B. Spill area of 60 feet or larger in diameter
    C. Spill area equal to or larger than 110 feet in diameter
    D. Any spill equal to or larger than a quarter-ton container

32. Approximately how soon after material release is a protective action zone in danger of being contaminated?
    A. 15 minutes
    B. 30 minutes
    C. 45 minutes
    D. 1 hour

33. What units of measure are used in the *ERG* to define the boundaries of the protective action zone?
    A. Square feet
    B. Square yards
    C. Tenths of miles
    D. Miles

34. Where should evacuees be sent so that they will not have to be moved again?
    A. *IERG/ERG* designated "safe" distance
    B. By specific route to a designated place upwind of the incident
    C. By specific route to a designated place at least 1 mile from the incident
    D. One mile upwind and uphill from the incident

IDENTIFICATION

Identify each of the following items.

35. External communication ____

36. Internal communication ____

37. Complaint ____

38. Hazard assessment ____

39. Nonintervention operation ____

40. Offensive operation ____

41. Defensive operation ____

42. Level I incident ____

43. Level II incident ____

6

44. Level III incident ____

45. Topographical aspect ____

46. Evacuation ____

47. Protection-in-place ____

48. Hot zone ____

49. Warm zone ____

50. Cold zone ____

Identify the following acronyms and abbreviations.

51. SARA ____

52. LERP ____

53. LEPC ____

54. EMO ____

55. SOP ____

56. *ERG* ____

57. *IERG* ____

58. IC ____

59. OSHA 1910.120 ____

60. NFPA 472 ____

61. NFPA 471 ____

62. HVAC ____

63. IFSTA ____

Identify the following levels by distinguishing between them.

64. Distinguish between the duties of a first responder at the awareness level and a first responder at the operational level. Write an "O" before those operational duties that are *additional* to awareness level duties that must be performed at both levels.

    A. _______ Define the problem.

    B. _______ Recognize the presence of hazardous materials.

    C. _______ Survey the incident from a safe distance to determine the identity of the materials involved.

    D. _______ Direct the execution of the incident action plan.

    E. _______ Secure the emergency area and prevent anyone from entering.

    F. _______ Call for the appropriate help to mitigate the incident.

    G. _______ Design a defense.

    H. _______ Determine the correct actions to be taken as recommended by the *ERG* or *IERG.*

65. Distinguish among examples of Level I, Level II, and Level III incidents. Write I, II, or III before appropriate examples.

    A. _______ Accident involving extremely hazardous substances

    B. _______ Small amount of gasoline spilled from an automobile

    C. _______ Incident that activates, in part or in whole, the federal response system

    D. _______ Spill or leak requiring large-scale evacuation

    E. _______ Spill or leak of unfamiliar or unknown chemicals

    F. _______ Small amount of diesel fuel spilled from a truck

    G. _______ Leak from domestic natural gas line on the consumer side of the meter

    H. _______ Incident beyond the capabilities of the local haz mat response team

    I. _______ Broken container of swimming pool chemicals at residential property

    J. _______ Major gas leak at service station

    K. _______ Incident that requires an evacuation extending across jurisdictional boundaries

    L. _______ Rupture of an underground pipeline

    M. _______ Fire that is posing a BLEVE threat

LISTING

66. List the seven areas that each LEPC must address when creating an LERP.

    A. ____

    B. ____

    C. ____

6

D. ____

E. ____

F. ____

G. ____

67. List ten pieces of information that should be gathered by the dispatcher from a person reporting a haz mat emergency.

A. ____

B. ____

C. ____

D. ____

E. ____

F. ____

G. ____

H. ____

I. ____

J. ____

68. List three responsibilities of the dispatcher on receiving a report of a haz mat incident.

A. ____

B. ____

C. ____

69. List the four functions that the first responder, operational level, must perform to define the problem at a haz mat scene.

A. ____

B. ____

C. ____

D. ____

70. List five tasks that may be performed by a first responder at the operational level when implementing an action plan.

A. ____

B. ____

C. ____

D. ____

E. ____

6

71. List the seven functions for which the incident commander is responsible.

    A. ____

    B. ____

    C. ____

    D. ____

    E. ____

    F. ____

    G. ____

72. List the five duties required of the safety officer during incident command.

    A. ____

    B. ____

    C. ____

    D. ____

    E. ____

73. List five pieces of hazard assessment information that can be obtained at the time of the alarm.

    A. ________________________   D. ________________________

    B. ________________________   E. ________________________

    C. ________________________

74. List six size-up responsibilities that can be considered by responders while en route.

    A. ____

    B. ____

    C. ____

    D. ____

    E. ____

    F. ____

75. List the five on-scene conditions that must be evaluated before a formal plan of action can be decided upon and implemented.

    A. ____

    B. ____

    C. ____

    D. ____

    E. ____

6

76. List the four circumstances that would probably lead to a nonintervention mode of operation.

A. ____

____

B. ____

____

C. ____

____

D. ____

____

77. List the six actions responders should take when operating in a nonintervention mode.

A. ____

B. ____

C. ____

D. ____

E. ____

F. ____

78. List the two circumstances that would lead to a defensive mode of operation.

A. ____

____

B. ____

____

79. List six actions first responders should take when operating in the defensive mode.

A. ____

____

B. ____

____

C. ____

____

D. ____

____

E. ____

____

F. ____
____

80. List criteria that one model uses to determine the level (severity) of a haz mat incident.

A. ____

B. ____

C. ____

D. ____

81. List the five specific responsibilities of first responders at a Level II haz mat incident.

A. ____

B. ____

C. ____

D. ____

E. ____

82. List resources and tasks that may be required to mitigate a Level III haz mat incident.

A. ____

B. ____

C. ____

D. ____

83. List five safety-related questions the incident commander should ask about personnel, procedures, and precautions before committing to action at a haz mat incident.

A. ____

B. ____

C. ____

D. ____

E. ____

84. List the seven aspects of the response that each responder should be made aware of during the incident briefing.

A. ____

B. ____

C. ____

D. ____

6

E. ____

F. ____

G. ____

85. List the four precautions the first responder should take to minimize the threat posed by the hazardous material involved in the incident.

A. ____

____

B. ____

____

C. ____

____

D. ____

____

86. List and explain the four container conditions that the first responder should observe during a haz mat incident.

A. ____

____

B. ____

____

C. ____

____

D. ____

____

87. List two ways of signaling a withdrawal in the event that the incident deteriorates.

A. ____

B. ____

88. List the ten potential ignition sources that must be eliminated if the hazardous material is explosive or flammable.

A. ____

B. ____

C. ____

D. ____

E. ____

F. ____

G. _______________________________________

H. _______________________________________

I. _______________________________________

J. _______________________________________

89. List five ways in which access to the initial isolation zone can be established and controlled.

A. _______________________________________

B. _______________________________________

C. _______________________________________

D. _______________________________________

E. _______________________________________

90. List three procedures that the responder would perform once evacuees have assembled in the designated assembly area.

A. _______________________________________

B. _______________________________________

C. _______________________________________

91. List three guidelines that help the responder determine to protect-in-place.

A. _______________________________________

____

B. _______________________________________

____

C. _______________________________________

____

92. List in order the actions needed when establishing scene control.

A. _______________________________________

B. _______________________________________

C. _______________________________________

D. _______________________________________

E. _______________________________________

F. _______________________________________

93. List three specific places that could serve as command posts.

A. _______________________________________

B. _______________________________________

C. _______________________________________

6

94. List three ways in which command posts may be identified.

A. ____

B. ____

C. ____

LABELING

95. Label the scene control zones and areas below. Write the correct names in the blanks corresponding to the lettered parts.

A. _________________________   F. _________________________

B. _________________________   G. _________________________

C. _________________________   H. _________________________

D. _________________________   I. _________________________

E. _________________________   J. _________________________

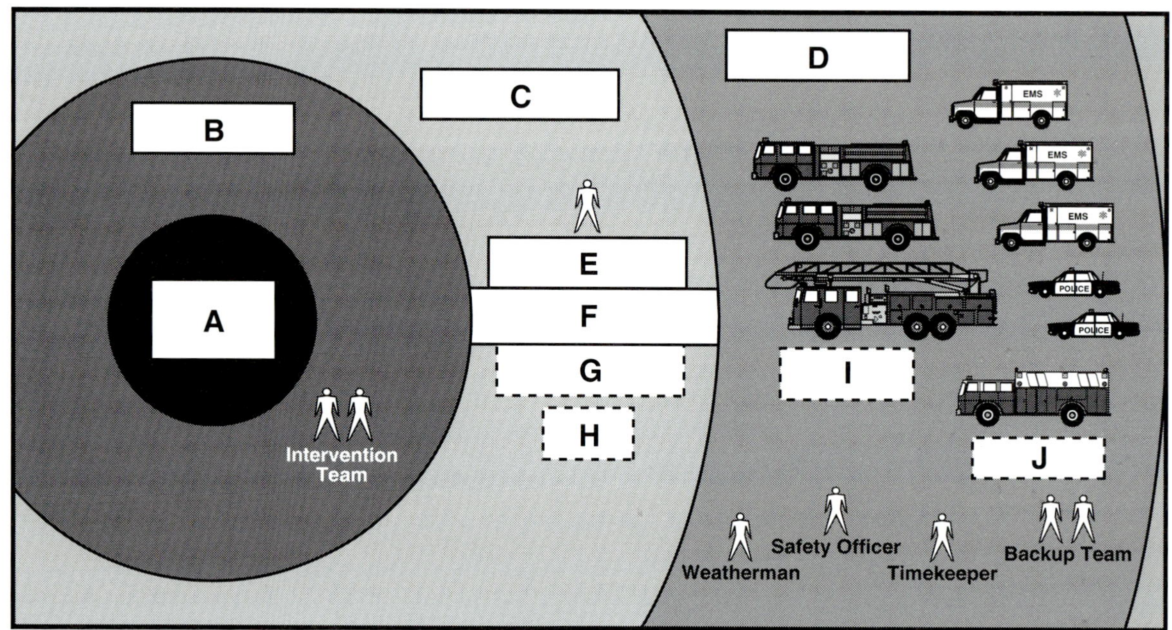

SHORT ANSWER

Briefly answer each question in your own words.

96. State the basic requirement of SARA.

____

____

97. Explain the following requirements of the command structure in an incident management system.

    A. Common terminology ____

    ____

    B. Modular organization ____

    ____

    C. Integrated communication ____

    ____

    D. Unified command structure ____

    ____

98. State in order of priority the three strategic goals upon which the incident commander develops a plan of action.

    A. ____

    B. ____

    C. ____

99. Provide a specific example to illustrate each of the following types of operations.

    A. Nonintervention ____

    ____

    B. Defensive ____

    ____

    C. Offensive ____

    ____

100. Which of the operations in question 99 is the upper limit of risk for first responders at the operational level?

    ____

101. Which of the operations in question 99 is beyond the scope of responsibilities for first responders at the awareness and operational levels?

    ____

102. Each responder must be able to recognize threats to his or her own safety. In general, how does the first responder accomplish this?

    ____

    ____

    ____

6

103. The following are aspects of the surroundings that the first responder must observe during a haz mat incident. Write the questions that the first responder must ask about each in regard to forming an action plan.

A. Weather

B. Topography

C. Water

D. Occupancies

E. Community transportation systems

F. Utilities

G. Zero energy state

104. According to the *ERG*, what is the difference between the "Initial Isolation Zone" and the "Protective Action Zone"?

A. Initial Isolation Zone

B. Protective Action Zone

____

____

105. What should evacuees of a haz mat area be told?

106. List the considerations in each of the following categories that the IC must take into account when selecting the best protective action or combination of actions.

A. Material considerations

B. Environmental conditions

C. Population at risk

107. What instructions should the responder give to people who are being protected-in-place?

108. When may protection-in-place *not* be the best protective action?

6

109. Explain why control zones are needed at haz mat incidents.

____

____

____

____

110. Discuss the purposes of the staging area.

____

____

____

____

____

Photo Courtesy of Scott D. Christiansen, Minot, N.D..

HAZ MAT

Tactical Priorities And Defensive Control Strategies

Tactical Priorities And Defensive Control Strategies | 7

Define each of the following terms.

1. Aerated

2. Breach

3. Diatomaceous earth

4. Dilution

5. Miscible

6. Polymeric

7. Proportioned

8. Surfactant

7

9. Turbulence

____

____

Mark each of the following statements true (T) or false (F). Correct each false statement.

10. ☐ T ☐ F When little is known about a material, the first responder should presume the worst-case scenario.

____

____

11. ☐ T ☐ F Fire streams can increase the intensity and size of a haz mat fire.

____

____

12. ☐ T ☐ F Confinement is primarily an offensive action.

____

____

13. ☐ T ☐ F Confinement is an offensive action that is performed at the awareness level.

____

____

14. ☐ T ☐ F Leak containment is usually performed before confinement of the spilled material, although both processes can be started simultaneously.

____

____

15. ☐ T ☐ F In most cases, first responders do not directly participate in recovery operations.

____

____

16. ☐ T ☐ F Contaminated construction materials used in confinement can be reused, but must be stored separately from other construction materials.

____

____

17. ☐ T ☐ F Generally, the foam application rate required to suppress vapors at an unignited liquid spill is substantially less than that required to extinguish a fire.

18. ☐ T ☐ F The greater the expansion ratio, the thicker the foam blanket that can be developed in a given period of time.

19. ☐ T ☐ F Water fog nozzles produce a larger expansion ratio than do air-aspirating nozzles.

20. ☐ T ☐ F All foams, except fluoroprotein types, should not be plunged directly into the spill but should be applied onto the ground at the edge of the spill and rolled gently onto the material.

21. ☐ T ☐ F Special foams for acid and alkaline spills are also very effective in fire suppression.

22. ☐ T ☐ F The person trained to extinguish flammable liquid fires is also qualified to mitigate vapors produced by haz mat spills.

23. ☐ T ☐ F Fire fighting foam is 94 to 99½ percent water.

24. ☐ T ☐ F Foams designed for hydrocarbon fires will extinguish polar solvent fires at higher concentrations.

7

25. ☐ T ☐ F Foams designed for polar solvents may be used on hydrocarbon fires.

____

____

26. ☐ T ☐ F Low-expansion foams are most effective when the fuel liquid exceeds 212°F (100°C).

____

____

27. ☐ T ☐ F The quantity of foam needed to extinguish a fire varies with the type of fuel.

____

____

28. ☐ T ☐ F Foam should be reapplied when the one-fourth lifetime limit of the foam has been reached or when vapor measuring equipment shows that the vapors being emitted from the spill are in the lower flammable range.

____

____

29. ☐ T ☐ F Regular protein foam is not commonly used today.

____

____

30. ☐ T ☐ F Regular protein foam should be applied by plunging the foam directly into the fuel.

____

____

31. ☐ T ☐ F Alcohol-resistant fluoroprotein foams maintain their alcohol-resistive properties in solutions for about 45 minutes.

____

____

32. ☐ T ☐ F When alcohol-type AFFFs are applied to polar solvent fuels, they create a membrane rather than a film over the fuel.

____

____

33. ☐ T ☐ F Hazardous materials vapor mitigating foam is the most commonly used foam for unignited haz mat spills.

____

____

MULTIPLE CHOICE

Circle the letter before the most appropriate response.

34. Which is NOT a category into which a material is placed during the identification process?
    A. Material is known and poses a substantial threat.
    B. Material is known and poses a minimal threat.
    C. Material is known and poses no immediate threat.
    D. Material is unknown.

35. Which of the following is NOT a miscible material?
    A. Diesel fuel
    B. Alcohol
    C. Ketones
    D. Esters

36. At what concentrations are Class A foams designed to be used?
    A. ½ or 1 percent
    B. 1 or 1½ percent
    C. 3 or 6 percent
    D. 1 to 6 percent

37. At what concentrations are foams for hydrocarbon fuels designed to be used?
    A. ½ or 1 percent
    B. 1 or 1½ percent
    C. 3 or 6 percent
    D. 1 to 6 percent

38. At what concentrations are foams for polar solvents designed to be used?
    A. ½ or 1 percent
    B. 1 or 1½ percent
    C. 3 or 6 percent
    D. 1 to 6 percent

39. At what concentrations are medium- and high-expansion foams typically used?
    A. 3, 4, or 6 percent
    B. 1, 1½, 2, or 3 percent
    C. 1 to 6 percent
    D. 1½, 2, or 6 percent

7

40. What is the typical expansion ratio range of medium-expansion foams?
    A. Between 10:1 and 20:1
    B. Between 20:1 and 2,000:1
    C. Between 20:1 and 200:1
    D. Between 200:1 and 1,000:1

41. What is the typical expansion ratio range of high-expansion foams?
    A. Between 10:1 and 20:1
    B. Between 20:1 and 2,000:1
    C. Between 20:1 and 200:1
    D. Between 200:1 and 1,000:1

42. Approximately how many gallons/liters of foam concentrate are typically needed to extinguish a tank truck fire and maintain a foam blanket in and around the tanker?
    A. 130
    B. 150
    C. 170
    D. 190

43. On what type of fire were protein foams designed to be used?
    A. Class A
    B. Class D
    C. Hydrocarbon
    D. Polar solvent

44. What is the most effective appliance for the generation of low-expansion foam?
    A. Standard fixed-flow fog nozzle
    B. Automatic foam nozzle
    C. Air-aspirating foam nozzle
    D. Standard water stream nozzle

45. With which of the following foam concentrates may a standard fixed-flow fog nozzle be used?
    A. FFFP
    B. AFFF
    C. Fluoroprotein
    D. Protein

IDENTIFICATION

Identify the following items.

46. Absorption ____

47. Defensive control ____

48. Dilution ____

7

49. Foam Quality Measure ____

50. (Foam) drainage time ____

51. (Foam) expansion ratio ____

52. Hydrocarbon fuel ____

53. Polar solvent fuel ____

54. Protein-based foam ____

55. Recovery ____

56. Subsurface injection ____

57. Synthetic-based foam ____

58. Vapor dispersion ____

59. Vapor suppression ____

60. Venturi principle ____

Identify each of the following terms related to foam generation.

61. Expansion ____

62. Foam concentrate ____

63. Foam proportioner ____

64. Foam solution ____

65. Finished foam ____

Identify proportioners and foam nozzles. Write the correct names in the blanks.

66. ___________________________   67. ___________________________

7

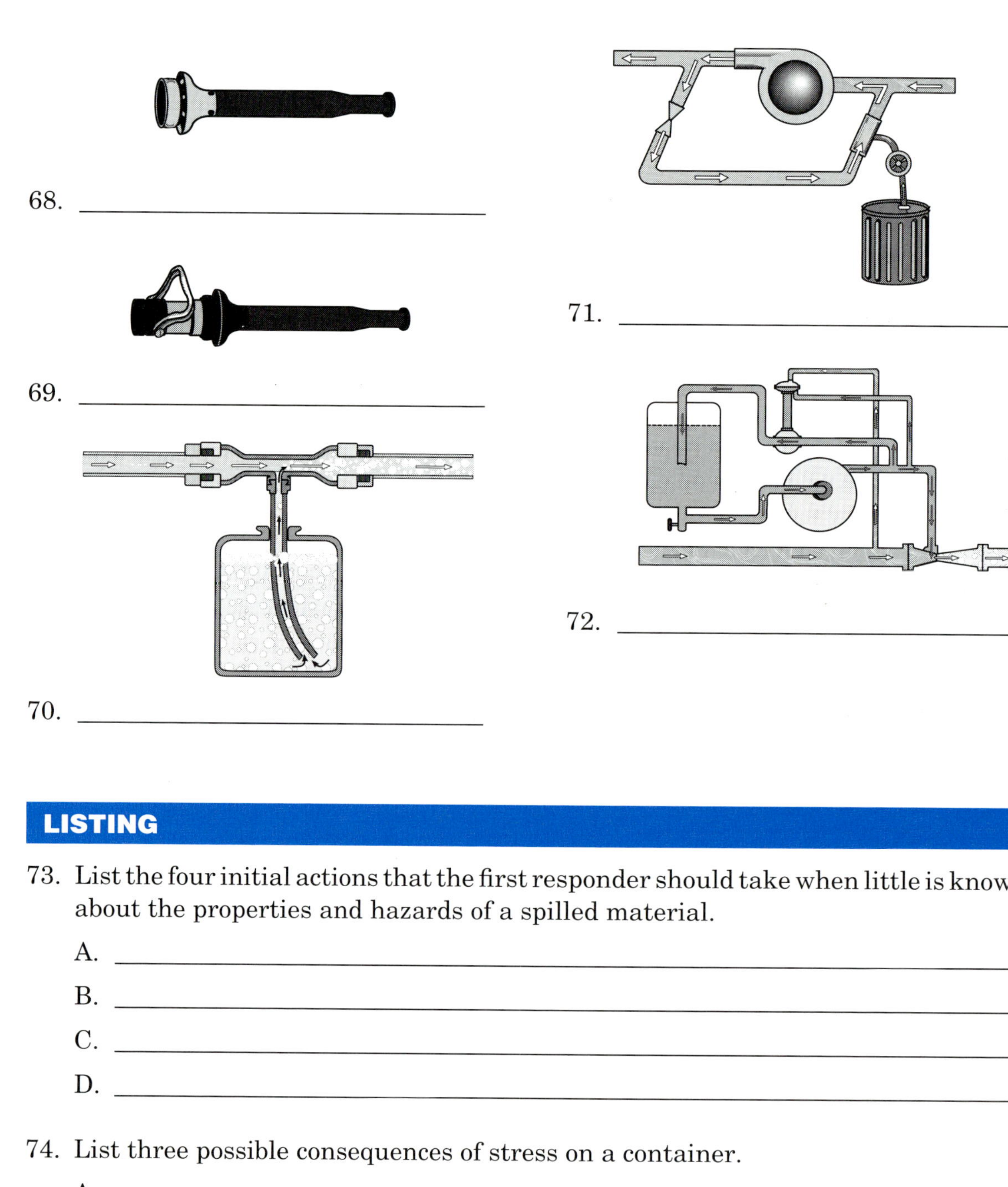

68. _______________________________

69. _______________________________

70. _______________________________

71. _______________________________

72. _______________________________

73. List the four initial actions that the first responder should take when little is known about the properties and hazards of a spilled material.

    A. ____

    B. ____

    C. ____

    D. ____

74. List three possible consequences of stress on a container.

    A. ____

    B. ____

    C. ____

75. List in order of highest to lowest the tactical priorities that must be considered and carried out for each incident.

    A. ____

    B. ____

    C. ____

    D. ____

7

E. ____

F. ____

76. List four factors that affect the ability of personnel to perform a rescue.

A. ____

B. ____

C. ____

D. ____

77. List in order of importance the tactical priorities that must be considered in exposure protection.

A. ____

B. ____

C. ____

78. List the three ways that hazardous materials liquid spills may be confined.

A. ____

B. ____

C. ____

79. List the six ways that haz mat dusts, vapors, and gases can be confined.

A. ____

B. ____

C. ____

D. ____

E. ____

F. ____

80. List five factors that determine which confinement measure(s) to use.

A. ____

B. ____

C. ____

D. ____

E. ____

7

81. List questions the first responder should ask in regard to containment conditions.

    A. The condition of the container

    ____

    ____

    B. The properties of the material

    ____

    ____

    ____

    C. The rate of release

    ____

    ____

    ____

    D. The incident assessment

    ____

    ____

82. List three common absorbents.

    A. ____

    B. ____

    C. ____

83. List five examples of hydrocarbon fuels.

    A. ___________________________   D. ___________________________

    B. ___________________________   E. ___________________________

    C. ___________________________

84. List and explain the four ways that foam extinguishes or prevents fire.

    A. ____

    B. ____

    C. ____

    D. ____

85. List the four elements necessary to produce a high-quality fire fighting foam.

    A. ___________________________   C. ___________________________

    B. ___________________________   D. ___________________________

86. What four pieces of equipment are needed to produce a foam fire stream?

    A. __________________________   C. __________________________

    B. __________________________   D. __________________________

87. List two operational mistakes that may cause automatic foam nozzle problems.

    A. ____

    B. ____

88. List six guidelines for installing an in-line proportioner.

    A. ____

    B. ____

    C. ____

    D. ____

    E. ____

    F. ____

89. List six of the most common reasons for failure to generate good-quality foam.

    A. ____

    B. ____

    C. ____

    D. ____

    E. ____

    F. ____

7

Briefly answer each question in your own words.

90. Distinguish between the actions necessary for confinement and containment.

    A. Confinement

    ____

    ____

    ____

    B. Containment

    ____

    ____

    ____

91. Distinguish between the actions necessary for vapor dispersion and vapor suppression.

    A. Vapor dispersion

    ____

    ____

    B. Vapor suppression

    ____

    ____

92. What two issues are of initial concern to haz mat first responders?

    A. ____

    ____

    B. ____

    ____

93. Who does the responder rescue first when there are several victims?

    ____

94. What is the difference between exposure protection as it applies to fires and exposure protection as it applies to haz mat incidents?

    A. Fire exposure protection _______________________________

    ____

    B. Haz mat exposure protection ___________________________

    ____

95. Explain the possible consequences of using foam or water on a flammable liquid spill.

____

____

____

____

96. When may the practice of letting hazardous materials burn be appropriate?

____

____

____

____

97. What are the objectives of confinement operations?

____

____

____

____

____

98. Name and explain the purposes of the three primary fire apparatus tools that may be used in confinement.

A. ____

B. ____

C. ____

99. Explain why dilution of liquid materials has few applications at a haz mat incident.

____

____

____

____

____

100. Explain how pressurized water streams help disperse vapor.

____

____

____

7

101. How is foam quality measured?

____

____

102. What exceptions are there to this statement: "All Class B foams may be used for both fire fighting and vapor suppression"?

____

103. Complete the following "points to consider when using foam for vapor suppression."

A. Foam is composed principally of water; therefore, _______________________

____

B. Some fuels destroy foam bubbles; therefore, _______________________

____

C. Water destroys and washes away foam blankets; therefore, _______________

____

D. Foam cannot seal vapors of boiling liquids; therefore, _______________________

____

E. Some films that precede the foam blanket, such as those with AFFF, cannot be

seen; therefore, _______________________________________

____

104. Explain, in general, how foam works to extinguish or prevent fire.

____

____

____

105. Explain the primary uses of low-, medium-, and high-expansion foams.

A. Low-expansion foam _______________________________________

____

B. Medium-expansion foam _______________________________________

____

C. High-expansion foam _______________________________________

____

106. Explain how medium- and high-expansion foams extinguish fires.

____

____

____

7

107. What is the difference between foam application rates for ignited fuels and those for unignited fuel spills?

108. Describe the two factors that usually limit the average fire department from effectively handling large containers (containers over 35-feet [10.7 m] in diameter) of burning fuels.

A.

B.

109. Briefly describe the following three types of foam proportioners.

A. Line eductor

B. Balanced pressure

C. Around-the-pump

110. Why are fluoroprotein foams ideally suited for direct foam application using a plunge technique?

111. What three things take place when AFFF or FFFP is applied to a hydrocarbon fire?

A.

B.

C.

7

112. Why is high-expansion foam generally not recommended for outdoor use?

____

____

113. Explain the differences between basic in-line eductor operation and variable pressure in-line eductor operation.

A. Basic in-line eductor operation

____

____

B. Variable pressure in-line eductor operation

____

____

114. List two operational mistakes that may cause automatic foam nozzle problems.

A. ____

B. ____

115. Explain the differences between the mechanical blower high-expansion foam generator and the water-aspirating high-expansion foam generator.

A. Mechanical blower

____

____

B. Water-aspirating

____

____

116. Complete the chart on the following two pages.

7

Type	Characteristics	Storage Range	Application Rate	Application Techniques	Primary Uses
Protein Foam					
Fluoroprotein Foam					
Film Forming Fluoroprotein Foam (FFFP)					
Aqueous Film Forming Foam (AFFF)					

7

Type	Characteristics	Storage Range	Application Rate	Application Techniques	Primary Uses
Alchohol-Resistant AFFF					
Medium- and High-Expansion Foam					
Class A Foam					

SOLVING PROBLEMS

7

117. Solve the following problems to calculate the quantity of foam concentrate needed for specified situations. Follow the steps below, and write your answers in the blanks.

Step 1: Refer to Table 7.1 below for general application rates per square foot and square meter.

Step 2: Multiply the application rate times the square feet/meters of fuel.

Step 3: Use the formula below to compute the amount of concentrate needed.

Application Rate x % Concentrate x 60 Minutes = Gallons / Liters Concentrate

Step 4: Divide your answer by 5 to convert total gallons (liters) to the number of 5-gallon (20 L) concentrate pails needed. Round your answers to the next whole number.

Table 7.1

	Fuel Type		
	Class A	**Polar Solvent**	**Hydrocarbon**
Application Rate (gpm per Ft^2/ $L/min/m^2$)	0.10/4.1	0.20/8.2	0.16/6.5
Percent Concentration	½ or 1%	3 or 6%	1 to 6%

A. ________ How many 5-gallon (20 L) pails of concentrate will you need for a 55-square-foot (5.1 m²) crude oil fire if you use 1 percent concentrate?

B. ________ If you use 3 percent concentrate, how many 5-gallon (20 L) pails of concentrate will you need for a dry cleaning establishment fire covering approximately 100 square feet (9.3 m²)?

C. ________ At 6 percent concentration, how many 5-gallon (20 L) pails of concentrate will you need for a gasoline transport tank truck fire covering approximately 400 square feet (37.2 m²)?

Chapter 8

HAZ MAT

Incident Control Strategies And Tactics

Incident Control Strategies And Tactics | 8

DEFINITIONS OF KEY TERMS

Define each of the following terms.

1. Bulk container *(as defined by DOT)*

2. Cartridge

3. Detonator

4. Dissipate

5. Emulsion

6. Etiological agent

7. Exothermal

8. Fissionable

8

9. Flame impingement

____

____

10. Half-life

____

____

11. Pressure vessel

____

____

12. Pyrophoric

____

____

13. Radiography

____

____

14. Radiopharmaceutical

____

____

15. Slurry

____

____

16. Water gel

____

____

TRUE/FALSE

Mark each of the following statements true (T) or false (F). Correct each false statement.

17. ☐ T   ☐ F   Most explosives (except for old or damaged explosives) will not detonate during proper handling.

____

____

8

18. ☐ T ☐ F   First responders must be prepared to neutralize or remove damaged or decomposed explosives.

____

____

19. ☐ T ☐ F   Large volume fire streams are desirable when fighting an external fire that does not involve the cargo or storage area containing explosives.

____

____

20. ☐ T ☐ F   The Canadian Transport Commission's requirements for the manufacture of gas pressure cylinders are the same as those developed by the U.S. Department of Transportation.

____

____

21. ☐ T ☐ F   All pressure cylinders and pressure tanks made of metal are aluminum, except for disposable lift-truck types that can be made of steel.

____

____

22. ☐ T ☐ F   The U.S. DOT regulates all U.S. compressed gas pipelines.

____

____

23. ☐ T ☐ F   Flames from a pressure-relief device should be extinguished to prevent flammable vapors from building up in the area and reigniting violently.

____

____

24. ☐ T ☐ F   First responders should not attempt to plug poisonous gas leaks not involving fire.

____

____

25. ☐ T ☐ F   Flammable gas tanks, as opposed to flammable liquid tanks, are not prone to BLEVE.

____

____

8

26. ☐ T   ☐ F   The DOT forbids the use of glass containers for shipping flammable and combustible liquids.

27. ☐ T   ☐ F   The construction material used most extensively in highway bulk containers is aluminum.

28. ☐ T   ☐ F   The construction material used most extensively in rail tank cars is aluminum.

29. ☐ T   ☐ F   Most new highway tankers are equipped with vapor recovery lines.

30. ☐ T   ☐ F   The vapors from flammable liquids are usually two or three times lighter than air.

31. ☐ T   ☐ F   Accidents involving flammable solids, spontaneously combustible materials, and materials that are dangerous when wet are relatively rare.

32. ☐ T   ☐ F   For the most part, extinguishment of Class 4 materials is not a primary objective for first responders.

33. ☐ T   ☐ F   Spontaneously combustible materials can be either liquids or gases.

34. ☐ T ☐ F   First responders generally do not have the resources needed to extinguish burning dangerous-when-wet materials.

35. ☐ T ☐ F   Most oxidizers are noncombustible but accelerate the burning of combustible materials.

36. ☐ T ☐ F   Oxidizers mixed with inorganic materials can ignite spontaneously.

37. ☐ T ☐ F   Some organic peroxides are shock sensitive, heat sensitive, and light sensitive.

38. ☐ T ☐ F   Organic peroxides may be shipped in tank trucks only with a special DOT permit.

39. ☐ T ☐ F   Hydrogen peroxide solutions are shipped in tank cars made of steel.

40. ☐ T ☐ F   Regulated medical wastes are included with infectious substances under DOT regulations.

41. ☐ T ☐ F   An accepted way to treat infectious substance incidents is to cover the container with a liquid-bleach-saturated towel.

8

8

42. ☐ T ☐ F   If a fire involving radioactive materials can be put out, first responders should do as thorough an overhaul as possible after extinguishment.

____

43. ☐ T ☐ F   Bases have a pH of 1 through 6.

____

44. ☐ T ☐ F   A pH of 7 is neutral.

____

45. ☐ T ☐ F   Corrosives can weigh up to twice that of an equal volume of water.

____

46. ☐ T ☐ F   Because of the density of corrosives, tanks used to transport them are larger than those used for other types of liquids.

____

47. ☐ T ☐ F   The primary objective in a corrosives spill fire is to protect exposures — not to extinguish the fire.

____

MULTIPLE CHOICE

Circle the letter before the most appropriate response.

48. What is the recommended distance away from an incident involving explosives and fire that all civilians and first responders should travel?
    A. 500 feet (155 m)
    B. 1,000 feet (310 m)
    C. 1,500 feet (465 m)
    D. 2,500 feet (775 m)

8

49. What is the pressure range for vessels holding compressed gas?
    A.   40 psi to 4,000 psi (276 kPa to 27 580 kPa)
    B.   30 psi to 3,000 psi (207 kPa to 20 685 kPa)
    C.   20 psi to 2,000 psi (138 kPa to 13 790 kPa)
    D.   10 psi to 1,000 psi (69 kPa to 6 895 kPa)

50. Pressure cylinders for gases range in size from the very small, hand-held types to those with a maximum capacity of how many pounds (kilograms)?
    A.   500 (227)
    B.   1,000 (454)
    C.   1,500 (680)
    D.   2,000 (907)

51. How does the first responder stop the flow of gas from a residential gas system?
    A.   Turns the gas meter petcock one-quarter turn clockwise
    B.   Turns the gas meter petcock until it is in a vertical position
    C.   Turns the gas meter petcock 90 degrees
    D.   Turns the gas meter petcock one-quarter turn counterclockwise

52. How far away should downwind ignition sources be considered if the incident involves LPG?
    A.   300 feet (93 m)
    B.   500 feet (150 m)
    C.   1,000 feet (310 m)
    D.   One-half mile (kilometer)

53. What is the purpose of water at a flammable gas tank fire?
    A.   Extinguishing the fire
    B.   Cooling the tank and reducing internal vapor pressure
    C.   Blanketing and confining airborne vapors
    D.   Dispersing vapors and extinguishing the fire

54. How long, on average, does it take large containers of LPG to fail violently on direct flame impingement?
    A.   10 to 20 minutes
    B.   15 to 30 minutes
    C.   5 to 10 minutes
    D.   20 to 30 minutes

55. Within how many feet (meters) do BLEVEs of large-capacity LPG containers typically create nonsurvivable conditions?
    A.   500 (150)
    B.   600 (186)
    C.   700 (217)
    D.   800 (248)

8

56. You are evacuating individuals from the area of an LPG tank that is about to BLEVE. What is the minimum distance that the evacuees must be taken to be safe from injury by tank shell fragments?
    A. 7,000 feet (2 170 m)
    B. 6,000 feet (1 860 m)
    C. 5,000 feet (1 550 m)
    D. 4,000 feet (1 200 m)

57. What is the minimum gpm (L/min) that should be played onto a large highway pressurized gas tanker or rail tank car at the point of flame impingement?
    A. 150 (570)
    B. 250 (1 000)
    C. 350 (1 325)
    D. 450 (1 704)

58. Approximately what size are pails of flammable or combustible liquids?
    A. 5 gallon (20 L)
    B. 10 gallon (40 L)
    C. 15 gallon (60 L)
    D. 20 gallon (80 L)

59. Which of the following steps would the first responder take when there is a leaking flammable liquid tank that threatens life or exposures?
    A. Apply a blanket of foam to the liquid pool.
    B. Disperse the liquid with hose streams.
    C. Dissipate the vapors with a fog stream above the liquid pool.
    D. Cool the container to prevent BLEVE.

60. What type of Class 4 materials are shipped in railroad tank cars?
    A. White phosphorous and sodium
    B. Solvents and motor fuels
    C. Chlorine or methyl bromide
    D. Organic peroxides

61. Which of the following is an example of a dangerous-when-wet material?
    A. White phosphorous
    B. Methyl bromide
    C   Perchloric acid
    D. Magnesium phosphide

62. Which of the following is an example of an oxidizer?
    A. White phosphorous
    B. Methyl bromide
    C   Perchloric acid
    D. Magnesium phosphide

8

63. Which of the following is NOT a resource for obtaining information about an infectious substance?
    A. CHEMTREC/CANUTEC
    B. Local hospital
    C. Center for Disease Control
    D. American Medical Association

64. What is the maximum capacity for tank trucks transporting corrosives?
    A. 6,000 gallons (24 000 L)
    B. 12,000 gallons (48 000 L)
    C. 18,000 gallons (72 000 L)
    D. 24,000 gallons (96 000 L)

MATCHING

Match hazards with their UN/DOT hazard classes. Write the correct letters in the blanks.

65. _______ Corrosives

66. _______ Explosives

67. _______ Flammable and combustible liquids

68. _______ Poisonous materials and infectious substances

69. _______ Radioactive materials

70. _______ Gases

71. _______ Oxidizers and organic peroxides

72. _______ Flammable solids, spontaneously combustible materials, and materials that are dangerous when wet

A. Class 1
B. Class 2
C. Class 3
D. Class 4
E. Class 5
F. Class 6
G. Class 7
H. Class 8

Match types of explosives with their packaging/shipping containers. Write the correct letters in the blanks. (See matching column on next page.)

73. _______ 1-pound (0.4 kg) metal can/fiberboard case; also large metal kegs or plastic bags/ fiberboard cases

74. _______ Various-sized paper or fiberboard cartridges/ spiral-wound fiberboard tubes, single tubes, or taped together to form bundles

8

75. ________ Multiwalled paper bag with a moisture-resistant plastic liner

76. ________ Plastic tubes or paper cartridges

77. ________ Spool/fiberboard case

78. ________ In bulk in special cargo trucks

79. ________ Fiberboard cartons/fiberboard case

A. Dynamite

B. Emulsions, slurries, water gels

C. Detonators

D. Detonating cord

E. Black powder, smokeless powder

F. Ammonium nitrate, fuel oil

G. Blasting agents, ammonium nitrate, fuel oil, certain emulsions, slurries, water gels

IDENTIFICATION

Identify the following abbreviations and acronyms.

80. DOT ____

81. CTC ____

82. CDC ____

83. API ____

84. ASME ____

85. BLEVE ____

86. SADT ____

Distinguish among characteristics of alpha, beta, and gamma radioactive materials. Write in the appropriate blanks an "A" for alpha, "B" for beta, and "G" for gamma.

87. ________ Moderate penetrating ability

88. ________ Least penetrating

89. ________ Similar to X rays

90. ________ Can penetrate clothing and human skin

91. ________ Extremely penetrating

8

92. ______ Aluminum foil will shield against particles

93. ______ Cannot penetrate clothing or human skin

94. ______ Travels nearly the speed of light

95. ______ Structural fire fighting clothing may not block particles

96. ______ Heavy particle

97. ______ Can penetrate all but the densest materials such as lead and thick concrete

98. ______ Travels only a few inches in the air

LISTING

99. List four places that commonly use and store explosives.

A. ________________________________   C. ________________________________

B. ________________________________   D. ________________________________

100. List those things from which explosives must be protected in order to prevent detonation.

A. ________________________________   D. ________________________________

B. ________________________________   E. ________________________________

C. ________________________________   F. ________________________________

101. List the six procedures the first responder should implement when confronted by an incident involving explosives but no fire.

A. ____

____

B. ____

____

C. ____

____

D. ____

____

E. ____

____

F. ____

____

8

102. List the essential procedures that first responders should perform when an explosive has already detonated.

A. ____

B. ____

C. ____

D. ____

103. List the three types of containers used to hold compressed gases.

A. ____

B. ____

C. ____

104. List six questions that first responders should ask immediately upon arrival at an incident involving gases.

A. ____

B. ____

C. ____

D. ____

E. ____

F. ____

105. List in order of importance the safety procedures to follow in any gas emergency.

A. ____

B. ____

C. ____

D. ____

E. ____

106. List the seven warning signals that indicate a pressurized gas tank may be in danger of imminent rupture.

A. ____

B. ____

C. ____

D. ____

E. ____

F. ____

G. ____

107. List three types of containers in which flammable or combustible liquids may be found.

    A. ____

    B. ____

    C. ____

108. List three examples of flammable or combustible liquids.

    A. ____

    B. ____

    C. ____

109. List three places where cans of flammable or combustible liquids are commonly found in large numbers.

    A. ____

    B. ____

    C. ____

110. List two types of flammable or combustible liquids commonly transported and stored in metal or plastic drums.

    A. ____

    B. ____

111. List five tactics for handling a leaking flammable liquid tank not involved in fire.

    A. ____

    ____

    B. ____

    ____

    C. ____

    ____

    D. ____

    ____

    E. ____

    ____

112. List six tactics that the first responder can initiate when dealing with a leaking flammable gas tank involving fire or flame impingement.

    A. ____

    ____

8

B. ___________________________

____

C. ___________________________

____

D. ___________________________

____

E. ___________________________

____

F. ___________________________

____

113. List three types of nonbulk packaging of Class 4 materials.

A. ___________________________

B. ___________________________

C. ___________________________

114. List the five questions that should be asked when it is suspected that a material is spontaneously combustible.

A. ___________________________

B. ___________________________

C. ___________________________

D. ___________________________

E. ___________________________

115. List three common methods of packaging oxidizers and organic peroxides.

A. ___________________________

B. ___________________________

C. ___________________________

116. List the five ways in which first responders can be harmed by poisonous substances.

A. ___________________________

B. ___________________________

C. ___________________________

D. ___________________________

E. ___________________________

117. List three Type A containers used to package and ship radioactive materials.

    A. ____

    B. ____

    C. ____

118. List two Type B containers used to package and ship radioactive materials.

    A. ____

    B. ____

119. List specific examples of three radioactive materials that would require Type B packaging.

    A. ____

    B. ____

    C. ____

120. List five types of containers in which both wet and dry corrosives are packaged.

    A. __________________________   D. __________________________

    B. __________________________   E. __________________________

    C. __________________________

121. List five guidelines for handling emergencies involving corrosive materials.

    A. ____

       ____

    B. ____

       ____

    C. ____

       ____

    D. ____

       ____

    E. ____

       ____

122. Provide three examples of specific emergencies that would involve flammable or combustible liquids.

    A. ____

    B. ____

    C. ____

8

Briefly answer each question in your own words.

123. Distinguish between poisonous materials and infectious substances.

    A. Poisonous materials ___________________________________

    ____

    B. Infectious substances ___________________________________

    ____

124. What are the two visual signs of explosives decomposition?

    A. ____

    B. ____

125. What is the immediate concern and primary objective for each of the following classes of hazardous materials?

    A. Explosives not yet on fire, but threatened

       Immediate concern ___________________________________

       Primary objective ____________________________________

    B. Explosives on fire

       Immediate concern ___________________________________

       Primary objective ____________________________________

    C. Nonflammable gas leaks not involving fire

       Immediate concern ___________________________________

       Primary objective ____________________________________

    D. Nonflammable gas leaks involving fire or flame impingement

       Immediate concern ___________________________________

       Primary objective ____________________________________

    E. Flammable gas leaks not involving fire

       Immediate concern ___________________________________

       Primary objective ____________________________________

    F. Flammable gas leaks involving fire or flame impingement

       Immediate concern ___________________________________

       Primary objective ____________________________________

G. Poisonous gas leaks not involving fire

Immediate concern ____

Primary objective ____

H. Poisonous gas leaks involving fire or flame impingement

Immediate concern ____

Primary objective ____

I. Spilled flammable/combustible liquids not involving fire

Immediate concern ____

Primary objective ____

J. Spilled flammable/combustible liquids involving fire or flame impingement

Immediate concern ____

Primary objective ____

K. Spilled flammable solids not involving fire

Immediate concern ____

Primary objective ____

L. Spilled flammable solids involving fire or flame impingement

Immediate concern ____

Primary objective ____

M. Spilled spontaneously combustible materials not involving fire

Immediate concern ____

Primary objective ____

N. Spilled spontaneously combustible materials involving fire or flame impingement

Immediate concern ____

Primary objective ____

O. Spilled dangerous-when-wet materials not involving fire

Immediate concern ____

Primary objective ____

P. Spilled dangerous-when-wet materials involving fire or flame impingement

Immediate concern ____

Primary objective ____

8

Q. Spilled oxidizers not involving fire

Immediate concern ____

Primary objective ____

R. Spilled oxidizers involving fire or flame impingement

Immediate concern ____

Primary objective ____

S. Spilled poisonous substances not involving fire

Immediate concern ____

Primary objective ____

T. Spilled poisonous substances involving fire

Immediate concern ____

Primary objective ____

U. Spilled infectious substances not involving fire

Immediate concern ____

Primary objective ____

V. Spilled infectious substances involving fire

Immediate concern ____

Primary objective ____

W. Spilled radioactive materials not involving fire

Immediate concern ____

Primary objective ____

X. Spilled radioactive materials involving fire

Immediate concern ____

Primary objective ____

Y. Spilled corrosive materials not involving fire

Immediate concern ____

Primary objective ____

Z. Spilled corrosive materials involving fire

Immediate concern ____

Primary objective ____

126. Why should runoff from incidents involving explosives be confined/collected?

127. What types of pressure containers *do not* have pressure-relief devices?

128. What is the most common type of compressed gas pipeline?

129. What is the most common container for flammable or combustible liquids?

130. How are pails of flammable or combustible liquids delivered to wholesalers and retailers?

131. What types of materials are categorized as flammable solids?

132. Why must first responders wear full protective clothing and SCBA in the proximity of combustible solids fires?

133. How are Class D dry powders applied to small metal fires?

134. When should dry powder *not* be used on small metal fires?

135. How are laboratory employees taught to handle a release of a spontaneously combustible material?

136. How do organic peroxide containers differ from similar containers used with other hazard class materials?

8

137. Why should first responders avoid walking into the oxidizing material when isolating an oxidizer spill?

____

____

____

138. Why are some organic peroxides kept refrigerated?

____

____

139. How are infectious substances packaged and shipped?

____

____

140. Distinguish between Type A packaging and Type B packaging of radioactive materials.

A. Type A packaging

____

____

B. Type B packaging

____

____

____

____

141. Describe the three ways that first responders can protect themselves from exposure to radiation.

A. ____

____

B. ____

____

C. ____

____

142. In what type of a container is hydrofluoric acid packaged/stored? Why?

____

143. Why should water not be used on corrosive materials?

____

____

Photo Courtesy of Scott D. Christiansen, Minot, N.D..

HAZ MAT

Decontamination Techniques

Decontamination Techniques | 9

DEFINITIONS OF KEY TERMS

Define each of the following terms.

1. Absorption

2. Chemical degradation

3. Contamination

4. Decontamination corridor

5. Dilution

6. Exposure

7. Impervious

8. Inert material

9

9. Secondary contamination

____

____

Mark each of the following statements true (T) or false (F). Correct each false statement.

10. ☐ T ☐ F First responders at the awareness level must be able to assist in decontamination techniques, which include selecting a decon site, setting up the corridor, and performing both basic and emergency decon.

____

____

11. ☐ T ☐ F Being exposed to a hazardous material does not necessarily mean that the exposed person or object is contaminated.

____

____

12. ☐ T ☐ F Threshold limit values are the same whether a solution contains 10 percent or 98 percent of a material.

____

____

13. ☐ T ☐ F The lower the TLV, the less hazardous the material.

____

____

14. ☐ T ☐ F Decontamination occurs in the cold zone.

____

____

15. ☐ T ☐ F Chemical degradation is never used on people who have been contaminated.

____

____

16. ☐ T ☐ F The first priority in selection of a decontamination site is its proximity to drains and waterways.

____

____

17. ☐ T ☐ F The floor area of the decon corridor should be covered only if the site surface is porous.

____

____

18. ☐ T ☐ F Water and solvents are the basic materials used for haz mat decontamination.

____

____

19. ☐ T ☐ F Awareness and operational level first responders must be prepared to neutralize caustic materials with weak hydrochloric acid solutions or neutralize acids with sodium carbonate solutions.

____

____

20. ☐ T ☐ F The decontamination site should be upwind of the hot zone.

____

____

21. ☐ T ☐ F The decontamination corridor should be established before any work is performed in the hot zone.

____

____

22. ☐ T ☐ F Emergency decontamination may be necessary even after basic decontamination is established.

____

____

IDENTIFICATION

Identify the following abbreviations and acronyms.

23. TLV ____

24. TLV-C ____

25. TLV-TWA ____

26. TLV-STEL ____

9

27. List four ways that first responders can become contaminated by a hazardous material.

    A. ____

    B. ____

    C. ____

    D. ____

28. List the three advantages of using dilution as a decontamination method.

    A. ____

    B. ____

    C. ____

29. List the two major disadvantages of using dilution as a decontamination method.

    A. ____

    B. ____

30. List the three advantages of using absorption as a decontamination method.

    A. ____

    B. ____

    C. ____

31. List the three disadvantages of using absorption as a decontamination method.

    A. ____

    B. ____

    C. ____

32. List four materials commonly used to change the chemical structure of a haz mat material.

    A. ____

    B. ____

    C. ____

    D. ____

33. List the two advantages of using chemical degradation as a decontamination method.

    A. ____

    B. ____

34. List the two disadvantages of using chemical degradation as a decontamination method.

    A. ____

    B. ____

35. List an advantage and a disadvantage of using isolation and disposal as a decontamination method.

    A. Advantage ____

    B. Disadvantage ____

36. List the six factors considered when choosing a decon site.

    A. _______________________________   D. _______________________________

    B. _______________________________   E. _______________________________

    C. _______________________________   F. _______________________________

37. List the four time periods crucial to decontamination site selection.

    A. ____

    B. ____

    C. ____

    D. ____

38. List six pieces of equipment and materials needed to set up a decon corridor.

    A. ____

    B. ____

    C. ____

    D. ____

    E. ____

    F. ____

39. List the steps in the basic decontamination procedure.

    Step 1: ____

    Step 2: ____

    Step 3: ____

    Step 4: ____

    Step 5: ____

    Step 6: ____

    Step 7: ____

9

40. List the three reasons for performing emergency decontamination.

    A. ____

    B. ____

    C. ____

SHORT ANSWER

Briefly answer each question in your own words.

41. Explain how the magnitude of the exposure to a hazardous material determines whether or not exposure to the material is harmful.

    ____

    ____

    ____

    ____

42. Explain how secondary contamination can occur.

    ____

    ____

43. Distinguish among basic, gross, and emergency decontamination procedures.

    A. Basic decontamination _______________________

    ____

    ____

    B. Gross decontamination _______________________

    ____

    ____

    C. Emergency decontamination ___________________

    ____

    ____

44. Explain the reasons for locating the decontamination site adjacent to the hot zone.

    ____

    ____

    ____

    ____

45. Explain why the decontamination site should ideally slope toward the hot zone.

46. What can first responders do if they cannot find the ideal slope for the decon site?

47. What can the first responder do if a hard surface for the decon site cannot be found?

48. In selecting a decon site, what should the first responder look for in terms of lighting?

49. How do some jurisdictions overcome the problem of cold winds when performing decon?

50. To what supplementary resources should the first responder refer to learn how to set up formal decontamination corridors?

HAZ MAT

Answers

Chapter 1 Answers

DEFINITIONS OF KEY TERMS

1. *Hazardous material* — A substance or material, including a hazardous substance, that has been determined by the Secretary of Transportation to be capable of posing an unreasonable risk to health, safety, and property when transported in commerce, and which has been so designated. (5)
2. *Dangerous good* — Any product, substance, or organism included by its nature or by the regulation in any of the classes listed in the schedule. (6)
3. *Hazardous waste* — Any material that is subject to the Hazardous Waste Manifest Requirements of the U.S. Environmental Protection Agency specified in 40 CFR, part 262. (5)
4. *Hazardous substance* —
   - Any substance designated via the Federal Water Pollution Control Act.
   - Any element, compound, mixture, solution, or substance designated pursuant to CERCLA.
   - Any hazardous waste having the characteristics identified under or listed pursuant to the Solid Waste Disposal Act (SWDA).
   - Any toxic pollutant listed under section 307(a) of the Federal Water Pollution Control Act.
   - Any hazardous air pollutant listed under section 112 of the Clean Air Act.
   - Any imminently hazardous chemical substance or mixture with respect to which the administrator has taken action pursuant to section 7 of the Toxic Substances Control Act. (5)
5. *Hazardous chemical* — Any chemical that is a physical hazard or a health hazard. (5)
6. *Extremely hazardous substance* — Any chemical that must be reported to the appropriate authorities if released above the threshold reporting quantity; hazardous substances listed and identified in Title III of Superfund Amendments and Reauthorization Act (SARA) of 1986. (6)
7. *Imminent* — Ready to take place. (Dict.)
8. *Pursuant* — In conformity with; according to. (Dict.)
9. *Awareness level* — Responsibility level of individuals who in the course of their normal duties find themselves first on the haz mat incident scene; their responsibilities include suspecting or recognizing the presence of a hazardous material, protecting themselves, calling for appropriate assistance, and securing the area. (9)
10. *Operational level* — Responsibility level of individuals who in the course of their normal duties find themselves first on the haz mat incident scene; their responsibilities include those four responsibilities of the awareness level individual, PLUS confining the release in a defensive fashion from a safe distance. (10)
11. *Etiological* — Biologically hazardous. (10, xvii)
12. *Repository* — A place, room, or container where something is placed or stored. (Dict.)
13. *Jurisdiction* — The limits or territory within which authority may be exercised. (Dict.)
14. *Rapport* — A relationship marked by harmony or conformity. (Dict.)

1

15. True (5)
16. False. CERCLA Section 101(14) *does not* include petroleum or any petroleum by-product, *unless it is specifically listed or designated as a hazardous substance.* (5)
17. True (6)
18. False. Dangerous goods are listed and identified in *Canadian schedule: "9 United Nations Classes of Hazardous Materials."* (6)
19. True (6)
20. False. Jurisdictions that do not have large manufacturing and storage facilities are *not completely void of hazardous materials in fixed locations. Hazardous materials will be encountered in seemingly ordinary locations.* (6, 7)
21. False. The three government agencies requiring that responders to haz mat incidents meet specific training standards are OSHA, EPA, and *WHMIS (Canada). HAZWOPER outlines OSHA regulations.* (8)
22. False. In addition to government regulations, *NFPA* has several standards that set requirements for personnel who respond to haz mat emergencies. (8)
23. False. A motor vehicle accident in which a truck loaded with hay overturns and its diesel fuel tanks begin to leak *would be considered a minor threat, not a major haz mat incident.* (8)
24. True (8)
25. False. First responders at the awareness level *do not contain spills.* They have only the responsibilities of 1) suspecting or recognizing the presence of a hazardous material, 2) protecting themselves, 3) calling for appropriate assistance, and 4) securing the area. (9)
26. True (9)
27. True (10)
28. True (11)
29. False. Many incidents *require the coordinated efforts of several agencies.* (11)

30. C (5)
31. D (6)
32. A (8)
33. A (8)
34. B (8)

35. *OSHA* — Occupational Safety and Health Administration (8)
36. *EPA* — Environmental Protection Agency (8)
37. *WHMIS* — Workplace Hazardous Materials Information System (Canadian) (8)
38. *HAZWOPER* — Hazardous Waste Operations and Emergency Response (8)
39. *NFPA* — National Fire Protection Association (8)
40. *DOT* — Department of Transportation (5)
41. *CFR* — Code of Federal Regulations (5, xiv)

42. *CERCLA* — Comprehensive Environmental Response, Compensation and Liability Act (5)
43. *SWDA* — Solid Waste Disposal Act (5)
44. *SARA* — Superfund Amendments and Reauthorization Act (6)
45. *CHEMTREC* — Chemical Transportation Emergency Center (11, xiv)
46. *CANUTEC* — Canadian Transport Emergency Centre (11, xiv)

47. *Haz mat incident* — Incident that involves a substance that has been released or is on fire, the material posing an unreasonable risk to people, the environment, and property; more complex than standard emergency incidents (8)
48. *Flammable liquid* — Any liquid having a flash point below 100°F (37.8°C) and having a vapor pressure not exceeding 40 psi absolute (276 kPa) (10, xviii)
49. *Heavy metal* — Generic term referring to lead, cadmium, mercury, and other elements that are toxic in nature (10, xx)
50. *Carcinogen* — Cancer-producing substance (10, xiv)
51. *Mutagen* — Material that causes changes in the genetic system of a cell in ways that can be transmitted during cell division or through heredity (10, xxiii)
52. *Teratogen* — Chemical that interferes with the normal growth of an embryo, causing malformations in the developing fetus (10, xxvii)

LISTING

53. A. Roadways
    B. Waterways
    C. Railways
    D. Airways
    E. Pipelines (6)
54. Answer should contain any five of the following locations:
    A. Service stations
    B. Hardware stores
    C. Doctors' offices
    D. School laboratories
    E. Agricultural stores or co-ops
    F. Farms
    G. Residences (7)
55. A. Methods of pre-incident planning, recognition, and incident control
    B. Types, properties, and characteristics of hazardous materials
    C. Methods of transporting and storing hazardous materials
    D. Proper handling of hazardous materials
    E. Appropriate defensive actions to take in emergencies involving hazardous materials
    F. Local, state, and federal regulations governing hazardous materials (7)
56. A. Human error
    B. Package failure
    C. Vehicle accidents/derailments (10)
57. A. Packaging
    B. Labeling
    C. Placarding

1

    D. Use

    E. Training of personnel

    F. Inspection and operation of fixed facilities

    G. Transportation vehicles and methods (10, 11)

58. A. Rescue

    B. Evacuation or sheltering-in-place

    C. Exposure protection

    D. Confinement or containment

    E. Emergency notification (11)

59. Answer should include any five of the following variables:

    A. Risk to rescuers

    B. Probability of victim survival

    C. Difficulty of rescue

    D. Capabilities and resources of on-scene forces

    E. Possibility of explosions or sudden material releases

    F. Available escape routes and safe havens

    G. Constraints of time and distance (11)

60. Answer should include any five of the following agencies:

    A. Fire service

    B. Law enforcement

    C. Emergency medical service

    D. Private concerns such as the material's manufacturer and shipper

    E. Government agencies with mandated interests such as health and environmental resources departments

    F. Various technical support groups such as CHEMTREC/CANUTEC

    G. Specialized emergency response groups (11)

SHORT ANSWER

61. A. *First responder awareness level*
    - First to suspect or recognize the presence of a hazardous material
    - Protect themselves
    - Call for appropriate assistance
    - Secure the area (9)

    B. *First responder operational level*
    - First to suspect or recognize the presence of a hazardous material
    - Protect themselves
    - Call for appropriate assistance
    - Secure the area
    - Confine the release in a defensive fashion from a safe distance (9, 10)

62. A. Vital resource information can be easily shared.

    B. Rapport between the participating agencies can be developed. (12)

63. For safety reasons, they must operate within the limitations of their training and act only within those parameters. (10)

64. Because all haz mat incidents can be viewed as learning experiences; documentation allows responders to examine the facts, analyze the incident, and critique their response so that they can avoid mistakes and use successful tactics and techniques on the next response. (10)

65. The potential for a haz mat incident can exist any time during the life of the material. Materials may be stored raw, mixed, or refined; ready-to-use or as a gas or liquid; and in quantities varying from very small packages to large, bulk containers. (10)

Chapter 2 Answers

DEFINITIONS OF KEY TERMS

1. *Acute* — Single occurrence. (15)
2. *Asphyxiant* — Hazardous material that affects oxygenation of the body and generally leads to suffocation. (19, xii)
3. *Avulsion* — The tearing off of part of the body. (19)
4. *Biochemical* — Involving chemical reactions in living organisms. (15)
5. *Chronic* — Long-term, reoccurring. (15)
6. *Condensation* — Process of moving from the gaseous to the liquid state. (30)
7. *Congenital* — Existing at or dating from birth. (24, xv)
8. *Corrosive* — Chemical exposure that destroys or burns living tissues and has destructive effects on other materials; may be acids or bases. (19)
9. *Cryogen* — A gas that turns into a liquid at or below -130°F (-90°C). (18)
10. *Dehydration* — The process of removing water or other fluids. (16, xvi)
11. *Dyspnea* — Painful or difficult breathing; rapid, shallow respiration. (23, xvii)
12. *Evaporation* — Process of a solid or liquid turning into a gas. (30)
13. *Flammability* — Ability to ignite easily and burn rapidly. (15)
14. *Inert* — Lacking chemical or biological action; inactive, nonreactionary. (Dict.)
15. *Inhibit* — To hold in check or discourage from activity. (Dict.)
16. *Lethal* — Deadly. (28, Dict.)
17. *Metabolism* — Conversion of food into energy and waste products. (28, xxiii)
18. *Olfactory* — Related to the sense of smell. (27, xxiv)
19. *Radioactive* — Emitting alpha, beta, and gamma radiation by the disintegration of the nucleus of atoms. (21, xxv)
20. *Reactive* — Process of reacting chemically with other substances; often, as in a chemical reaction, changing the composition of one substance by converting it to another. (31, xxv)
21. *Stimulus* — Something that arouses or incites to activity. (Dict.)
22. *Suffocate* — To die from being unable to breathe; to be deprived of air or to stop respiration as by strangulation or asphyxiation. (20, xxvii)
23. *Thermal* — Relating to or caused by heat. (16)
24. *Vapor pressure* — Measure of the tendency of a substance to evaporate. (31)

TRUE/FALSE

25. False. Symptoms of *heatstroke* include lack of perspiration; hot, red, dry skin; and confusion. (16, Table 2.2)
26. False. The first responder should *avoid* drinking carbonated beverages before and during operations. (17)

2

27. True (17)
28. True (18)
29. False. Liquefied gases can cause freeze burns, which are treated like *cold injuries* according to their severity. (18)
30. False. Pain is associated with contacting an acid; *a base does not normally cause immediate pain* but instead produces a slick feeling of the skin caused by breakdown of fatty tissue. (20)
31. False. *Chemical asphyxiants* are also called blood poisons. (20)
32. True (21)
33. False. Radiation sickness, injury, and poisoning are *not* infectious or contagious. (21)
34. True (21)
35. False. *Beta* radiation particles have a negative electrical charge; alpha radiation particles have a positive electrical charge. (21)
36. True (21)
37. True (22)
38. True (22)
39. False. In general *gases* pose more of a potential danger to first responders than do *liquids*. (27)
40. True (27)
41. False. The *lower* the LC_{50} values, the more toxic a substance. (28)
42. True. The vapors from flammable liquids ignite, but the liquids themselves do not burn. (29)
43. False. Propane gas is *heavier* than air. (30)
44. True (27)
45. True (30)

MULTIPLE CHOICE

46. D (23, 24)
47. B (16, Table 2.2)
48. A (17)
49. A (18)
50. C (19)
51. B (19)
52. D (20)
53. C (20)
54. A (20)
55. C (20)
56. B (21)
57. A (22)
58. C (22)
59. C (22)
60. D (22)
61. D (22)
62. C (22)
63. A (22)
64. B (23)
65. A (24)
66. C (24)
67. B (24)
68. A (27)
69. D (30)
70. C (31)

MATCHING

71. C
72. B
73. A
74. D (25)

75. C
76. A
77. D
78. B (31, 32)

79. A
80. D
81. C
82. B (19)

83. C
84. A
85. D
86. B
87. E (21, 22)

88. I
89. B
90. A
91. C
92. J
93. K
94. D
95. F
96. E
97. G
98. L
99. M
100. H (15 - 24)

IDENTIFICATION

101. American Conference of Governmental Industrial Hygienists (27)
102. Parts per million (28)
103. Milligrams per cubic meter (28)
104. Milligrams per liter (28)
105. Threshold Limit Value/Time-Weighted Average (27)
106. Threshold Limit Value/Short-Term Exposure Limit (28)
107. Threshold Limit Value/Ceiling Level (28)
108. Permissible Exposure Limit (28)
109. Lethal Dose (28)
110. Lethal Concentration (28)
111. Immediately Dangerous to Life and Health (28)

112. Classification of ACGIH recommended exposure limits; based on time-weighted averages, short-term exposure limits, and ceiling levels (27)
113. The maximum airborne concentration to which an average, healthy person may be exposed repeatedly for 8 hours each day, 40 days per week without suffering adverse effects (27)
114. The 15-minute, time-weighted average exposure that should not be exceeded at any time or repeated more than four times a day; requires a 60-minute rest period between each exposure (28)
115. The maximum concentration that should never be exceeded (28)
116. Classification of OSHA recommended exposure limits; based on maximum allowable exposure for an 8-hour day (28)

2

117. The minimum amount of solid or liquid that when ingested, absorbed, or injected through the skin will be fatal to 50 percent of all subjects exposed to that dosage (28)
118. The minimum concentration of an inhaled substance in the gaseous state that will be fatal to 50 percent of the test group (28)
119. Any toxic, corrosive, or asphyxiating substance that poses an immediate threat to life (28)

120. Minimum temperature at which a liquid fuel gives off sufficient vapors to form an ignitable mixture with air near its surface (29)
121. Minimum temperature at which enough vapors are given off to support continuous burning (29)
122. Minimum temperature to which the fuel in air must be heated to initiate self-sustained combustion without initiation from an independent ignition source (29)
123. Percentage of the gas or vapor concentration in air that will burn if ignited (29)
124. Weight of a substance compared to the weight of an equal volume of water at a given temperature (30)
125. Density of a gas compared to the density of an equal volume of air (30)
126. Temperature at which a substance most rapidly changes from a liquid to a gas or when the rate of evaporation exceeds the rate of condensation (30)
127. A flammable liquid's ability to mix with water (31)

128. A. Below 100°F (38°C)
    B. Above 100°F (38°C)
    C. No flashpoints because they are already in the gaseous state
    D. With the exception of a few solids, such as napthalene with a flashpoint of 174°F (70°C), solids do not have flashpoints. (29)

LISTING

129. A. Muscle cramps
    B. Heavy perspiration
    C. Physical weakness
    D. Moist skin (16, Table 2.2)
130. A. Mildly elevated temperature
    B. Weak pulse
    C. Dizziness
    D. Profuse sweating
    E. Cool, moist, pale skin (16, Table 2.2)
131. A. Body temperature of 105°F (41°C) or higher
    B. Rapid pulse
    C. Confusion
    D. Lack of perspiration
    E. Hot, dry, red skin
    F. Shallow breathing
    G. Weakness
    H. Headache
    I. Convulsion
    J. Loss of consciousness (16, Table 2.2)

2

132. Answer should include any six of the following guidelines:
     A. Drink plenty of fluids.
     B. Provide for natural body ventilation by wearing long cotton underwear or similar type of clothing.
     C. Use mobile showers or misting facilities.
     D. Take advantage of shaded and air-conditioned rest areas.
     E. Rotate out of difficult tasks or those involving extreme temperatures.
     F. Avoid drinking alcohol, coffee, and caffeinated drinks.
     G. Maintain your physical fitness. (17, 18)
133. A. Burning around the eyes, nose, and mouth
     B. Nausea and vomiting
     C. Difficulty breathing, swallowing, or coughing
     D. Localized burning and skin irritation (20)
134. Answer may include any four of the following simple asphyxiants, but may include other appropriate examples approved by the instructor:
     A. Acetylene
     B Carbon dioxide
     C. Helium
     D. Hydrogen
     E. Nitrogen
     F. Methane
     G. Ethane (20)
135. Answer may include any four of the following chemical asphyxiants, but may include other appropriate examples approved by the instructor:
     A. Carbon monoxide
     B. Hydrazine
     C. Benzene
     D. Toulene
     E. Hydrogen cyanide
     F. Aniline
     G. Acetonitrile
     H. Hydrogen sulfide (20)
136. Answer may include any three of the following diseases, but may include other appropriate examples approved by the instructor:
     A. Hepatitis
     B. AIDS
     C. Tuberculosis
     D. Typhoid (19, 23)
137. Answer may include any two of the following convulsants, but may include other appropriate examples approved by the instructor:
     A. Strychnine
     B. Organophosphate
     C. Carbamates
     D. Picrotoxin (23)
138. Answer may include any five of the following known or suspected carcinogens, but may include other appropriate examples approved by the instructor:
     A. Polyvinyl chloride
     B. Asbestos

2

    C. Chlorinated hydrocarbons
    D. Arsenic
    E. Nickel
    F. Some pesticides
    G. Many plastics
    H. Smoke (23)

139. Answer may contain any two of the following mutagens, but may include other appropriate examples approved by the instructor:
    A. Radiation exposure
    B. Benzene
    C. Ethylene oxide (24)

140. Answer may include any four of the following teratogens, but may include other appropriate examples approved by the instructor:
    A. Ionizing radiation
    B. Ethyl alcohol
    C. Methyl mercury
    D. Thalidomide
    E. Dioxins
    F. Rubella infection (24)

141. Answer may include any three of the following toxic products of combustion, but may include other appropriate examples approved by the instructor:
    A. Hydrogen cyanide
    B. Carbon monoxide
    C. Hydrogen chloride
    D. Acrolein (31)

142. Answer may include any two of the listed examples for each of the following materials, but may include other appropriate examples approved by the instructor:
    A. *Unstable material* — Picric acid, ether, dynamite, organic peroxides, nitroglycerin (31)
    B. *Hypergolic material* — LOX and asphalt, macadam, or blacktop; rocket fuels such as nitric acid and hydrazine or nitrogen tetroxide and hydrazine (31)
    C. *Pyrophoric material* — White phosphorus, molten sodium, cesium, potassium, aluminum alkyls, rubidium, powdered titanium, powdered uranium (32)
    D. *Water-reactive material* — Lithium, finely divided magnesium, potassium, rubidium, sodium, cesium, calcium carbide (32)

LABELING

143. A. Upper respiratory tract
    B. Lower respiratory tract
    C. Deep respiratory tract
    D. Main bronchus
    E. Trachea
    F. Mouth
    G. Nose
    H. Pharynx
    I. Larynx
    J. Bronchioles
    K. Alveoli
    L. Lungs (23, Figure 2.9)

SHORT ANSWER

144. A. *Carcinogens* — Cancer-causing agents
   B. *Mutagens* — Materials that cause changes in the genetic system of a cell in ways that can be transmitted during cell division
   C. *Teratogens* — Cause congenital malformation (23, 24)
145. A. *Somatic effect* — Causes injury to exposed individuals
   B. *Genetic effect* — Causes changes in future generations (21)
146. A. *Acids* — Cause severe chemical burns to flesh and permanent eye damage
   B. *Bases* — Break down fatty skin tissues and can penetrate deeply into the body (20)
147. A. *Simple asphyxiants* — Displace oxygen needed for breathing
   B. *Chemical asphyxiants* — Prohibit the body from using oxygen (20)
148. A. *Radiation sickness* — Caused by exposure to large amounts of radiation; symptoms include nausea, vomiting, and malaise
   B. *Radiation injury* — Generally caused by external exposure to high amounts of less-penetrating types of radiation; signs include radiation burns, especially to the hands
   C. *Radiation poisoning* — Caused by dangerous amounts of internal radiation; no specific symptoms given, but may result in anemia or cancer (21)
149. A. *Time* — The shorter the exposure time, the smaller the total radiation dose
   B. *Distance* — The farther the distance from the source, the smaller the dose
   C. *Shielding* — Certain materials such as lead, earth, concrete, and water, will stop the penetration of some radiation particles (22)
150. A. *Polar solvents* — Water-soluble flammable liquids
   B. *Hydrocarbons* — Nonwater-soluble flammable liquids (31)
151. A. *Hypergolic materials* — Ignite when coming into contact with each other and involve the mixing of a chemical fuel and an oxidizer
   B. *Pyrophoric materials* — Elements that react and unite on contact with air (32)

Chapter 3 Answers

DEFINITIONS OF KEY TERMS

1. *Carboy* — A large bottle of glass, plastic, or metal, often cushioned in a special protective container. (90, xiv)
2. *Consignee* — One to whom something is shipped. (50, xv)
3. *Contingency* — Something that is likely but not certain to happen dependent on something else; possibility. (Dict.)
4. *Frangible* — Readily or easily broken. (79, xix)
5. *Intermodal* — Freight containers designed and constructed to permit them to be used interchangeably in two or more modes of transport. (86)
6. *Outage* — Difference between the full or rated capacity of a tank or tank car as compared to actual content. (85, xxi)
7. *Polymerization* — Reactions in which two or more molecules chemically combine to form larger molecules; reaction often violent. (51, xxv)

3

8. *Prilled* — Converted into spherical pellets. (64, Table 3.4)
9. *Tare* — A deduction from the gross weight of a substance and its container made in allowance for the weight of the container. (74, xxvii)
10. *Volatile* — (1) Changing into vapor quite readily at a fairly low temperature (2) Tending to erupt into violence; explosive. (44, xxix)

TRUE/FALSE

11. False. Shipped cryogenic materials *require placards only if they are shipped in excess of 1,000 pounds.* (76, Table 3.8)
12. True (76)
13. False. Flammable solids are *not* shipped in marine tankers *but may be shipped by barge or tank car.* (78, Table 3.9)
14. True (78, Table 3.9)
15. True (78, Table 3.9)
16. True (78, Table 3.9)
17. False. In NFPA 704 markings, the health hazard rating appears at the *nine o'clock* position. (56)
18. True (40)
19. True (43)
20. False. At the onset of physical symptoms of chemical exposure, those people exposed should *immediately withdraw to a safe location for decontamination, treatment, and observation or medical treatment.* (44)
21. False. *Not* all chemical exposures result in immediate symptoms; *symptoms may not appear until hours after exposure.* (45)
22. False. Explosives are *not* listed individually in the *ERG* by identification number. (48)
23. False. Highlighted entries in the *ERG* indicate that the *material represents poison and poison inhalation risks and that there is no fire involved with the incident.* (48)
24. False. When first responders using Canada's *IERG* cannot identify a hazardous material by its identification number, name, placard, or container shape, they should refer to *Guide 01.* (49)
25. True (48)
26. True (49)
27. True (49)
28. True (49, 50)
29. True (50)
30. True (50)
31. False. U.S. material safety data sheets *are not accepted in Canada because they are slightly different from the Canadian MSDS.* (54)
32. False. The first responder should consult a minimum of *two* resources for information about a material. (54)
33. False. A hazardous material is most easily identified *before* it is released from its container. (54)
34. False. Hazardous materials that are manufactured, stored, processed, or used at a fixed facility *are not subject to regulations affecting transported materials.* (55)
35. False. The NFPA 704 system *does not* identify the specific chemical or chemicals that may be present. (57, Table 3.3)

36. True (65)
37. True (76)
38. False. Some refrigerated boxcars carry up to 500 gallons (2 000 L) of *diesel fuel* for cooling system power generation. (86)
39. False. A white railcar with a red horizontal stripe around it and two vertical red stripes 3 feet (1 m) from each end always hauls *hydrogen cyanide (hydrocyanic acid).* (85)
40. False. Even if the first responder recognizes the cargo tank truck, *the process of positive identification must proceed from placards, shipping papers, or other formal sources of information.* (77)
41. True (82)
42. True (83)
43. False. If a tank railcar is classified "DOT-115," it is a *nonpressurized* railcar. (84)
44. True (84)
45. True (84)
46. False. Most tank cars that carry *corrosive materials* are either loaded or unloaded from the top and have no plumbing underneath. (84)
47. True (86)
48. False. General service tank railcars are *not* distinguishable from those transporting hazardous materials, *unless the tank railcars are required to carry commodity names or to display placards.* (84)
49. True (93)
50. True (93)
51. False. The first responder is *not expected to know how to operate and interpret monitoring instruments.* (94)

MULTIPLE CHOICE

52. B (76, Table 3.7)	71. D (76)
53. D (76, Table 3.8)	72. B (76)
54. C (76, Table 3.7)	73. D (76)
55. A (78, Table 3.9)	74. C (76)
56. A (78, Table 3.9)	75. D (79)
57. D (78, Table 3.9)	76. B (80)
58. C (78, Table 3.9)	77. B (80)
59. A (46)	78. A (81)
60. C (47)	79. C (82)
61. C (48)	80. D (83)
62. B (48)	81. D (88)
63. C (49)	
64. A (50)	
65. D (51)	
66. C (55)	
67. B (64, Table 3.4)	
68. A (73)	
69. A (76)	
70. C (76)	

3

82. D
83. A
84. E
85. B
86. C (57, Table 3.3)

87. E
88. D
89. B
90. C
91. A (57, Table 3.3)

92. B
93. A
94. E
95. C
96. D (57, Table 3.3)

97. A
98. D
99. E
100. B
101. C
102. E (46-48, Table 3.1)

103. B
104. A
105. C
106. D
107. D
108. C (48, 49, Table 3.2)

109. D
110. B
111. A
112. F
113. C
114. E (46-48)

115. C (58)
116. D (60)
117. B (58)
118. G (60)
119. E (58)
120. L (60)
121. K (62)

122. J (60)
123. F (61)
124. H (61)
125. A (62)
126. I (58)

127. D
128. A
129. B
130. E
131. C
132. F (63)

133. I
134. F
135. H
136. A
137. B
138. D
139. G
140. C
141. E (63)

142. C
143. F
144. B
145. D
146. E
147. A (70)

148. D
149. B
150. C
151. A (70)

152. H
153. D
154. J
155. B
156. C
157. A
158. F
159. I
160. K
161. G
162. E (64)

163. G
164. F
165. C
166. I
167. H
168. D
169. A
170. E
171. B (65-67)

172. I
173. E
174. F
175. A
176. C
177. B
178. D
179. H
180. G (65-67)

181. H
182. A
183. C
184. L
185. J
186. D
187. E
188. A
189. M
190. G
191. A
192. K
193. B
194. I
195. F
196. A
197. A (65-67)

198. G
199. G
200. G
201. D
202. B
203. E
204. B
205. G

206. F
207. A
208. C (NFPA 704 and NFPA 49)

209. C (77)
210. A (79)
211. D (82)
212. G (80)
213. F (80, 81)
214. B (81)
215. H (82)
216. E (82)

217. C (84, 85)
218. A (84)
219. B (83)

220. A
221. G
222. E
223. D
224. C
225. F
226. B (91)

227. H
228. B
229. I
230. F
231. A
232. C
233. G
234. D
235. E (92)

IDENTIFICATION

236. National Response Team (39)
237. *Emergency Response Guidebook* (45)
238. Department of Transportation (45)
239. *Dangerous Goods Guide to Initial Emergency Response* (45)
240. United Nations/North America (46)
241. Product identification number (49)
242. National Response Center (50)
243. National Agricultural Chemical Association (51)
244. Liquefied petroleum gas (51, xxii)
245. Liquefied natural gas (61)
246. Compressed Gas Association (xiv)
247. Material Safety Data Sheet (51)
248. National Toxicological Program (54)
249. International Agency for Research on Cancer (54)
250. Chemical Abstract Service (52, xiv)
251. Hazardous Materials Transportation Act (63)
252. Transport Development Group (63)
253. Nuclear Regulatory Commission (63)
254. Environmental Protection Agency (63)
255. Department of Energy (63)
256. Occupational Safety and Health Administration (63)
257. Other regulated materials (63)
258. Liquid oxygen (81)
259. Trailers on flatcars (86)
260. Containers on flatcars (86)
261. Intermodal (87, Table 3.11)
262. Pest Control Product (92)
263. Polychlorinated biphenyl (93)

3

264. United States
265. Singapore
266. Bermuda
267. China (States)
268. Panama
269. Netherlands
270. Korea
271. Italy
272. Hong Kong
273. France
274. West Germany
275. Bermuda
276. Panama
277. Sweden
278. China (Taiwan)
279. Phillipines
280. Netherlands
281. Liberia
282. Japan
283. Israel
284. Great Britain
285. Denmark
286. Switzerland
287. Japan
288. France
289. Switzerland (88, Table 3.12)

290. Cryogenic-liquid storage tank (62)
291. Lifter roof atmospheric tank (59)
292. Floating roof atmospheric tank (59)
293. Spheroid low-pressure tank (60)
294. Ordinary cone roof atmospheric tank (58)
295. Horizontal tank pressure vessel (61)
296. Vapordome roof atmospheric tank (60)
297. Sphere tank pressure vessel (62)
298. Internal floating roof atmospheric tank (59)
299. Noded spheroid low-pressure tank (61)
300. Underground storage tank (62)
301. Horizontal atmospheric tank (60)

302. *NFPA 704* — National Fire Protection Association standard containing a haz mat identification system (55)
303. *NFPA 30* — National Fire Protection Association *Flammable and Combustible Liquids Code* (71)
304. *NFPA 49* — National Fire Protection Association *Hazardous Chemicals Data* (56)
305. *UN haz mat identification number* — Four-digit number assigned to each material listed in the *ERG* or *IERG* (46)
306. *Dedicated railcar* — A railcar set aside by a material manufacturer to transport a single material (85)

3

307. *Bulk packaging* — Packaging other than a vessel or a barge in which hazardous materials are loaded with no intermediate form of containment (90)
308. *Assessment stop* — Distant location at which it is safe for first responders to stop and evaluate the situation, to complete donning their protective clothing and SCBA, and to report conditions to the communications center (43)
309. *CAS number* — Number assigned by the American Chemical Society's Chemical Abstract Service that uniquely identifies a specific compound (52, xiv)
310. *Christmas tree vent* — Combination vacuum breaker and relief device (79)

311. Air bill
312. Cockpit
313. Pilot
314. Bill of lading
315. Cab of vehicle
316. Driver
317. Waybill/consist
318. Engine or caboose
319. Conductor
320. Dangerous cargo manifest
321. Bridge or pilot house
322. Captain or master (73, Table 3.6)

323. *Mass explosion hazard* — An explosion that affects almost the entire load instantaneously (70)
324. *Flammable liquid* — A liquid having a flash point of not more than 141°F (61°C) or any material in a liquid phase with a flash point at or above 100°F (38°C) that is intentionally heated (mixtures and solutions) and offered for transportation or transported at or above its flash point in a bulk packaging OR a distilled spirit of 140 proof or lower having a flash point of no lower than 73°F (23°C) (70)
325. *Combustible liquid* — Any liquid that does not meet the definition of any other hazard class, except Class 9, and has a flash point above 141°F (61°C) and below 200°F (93°C) OR a flammable liquid with a flash point at or above 100°F (38°C) that does not meet the definition of any other hazard class, except Class 9 (71)
326. *Oxidizer* — A material that may, generally by yielding oxygen, cause or enhance the combustion of other materials (71)
327. *Infectious substance* — An etiological agent that is a viable microorganism, or its toxin, that causes or may cause disease in humans or animals (71)

328. Dry bulk carrier (83)
329. MC-312/DOT-412 corrosive liquid carrier (80)
330. MC-338 cryogenic liquid carrier (82)
331. Compressed gas trailer (tube trailer) (82)
332. MC-331 high-pressure carrier (81)
333. Elevated-temperature materials carrier (83)
334. MC-306/DOT-406 atmospheric pressure (nonpressure) carrier (77)
335. MC-307/DOT-407 low-pressure carrier (79)

336. Cryogenic-liquid tank railcar (85)
337. Nonpressure tank railcar (84)
338. Pressure tank railcar (83)

3

339. CY
340. P
341. NP
342. DR
343. CY
344. NP
345. P
346. DR
347. NP
348. CY
349. NP
350. NP
351. P
352. C
353. DR (83-86)

354. IMO Type 2/IM 101 portable nonpressure tank (89)
355. IMO Type 5/DOT Spec 5 pressure tank (89)
356. IMO Type 1/IM 102 portable nonpressure tank (89)

357. *Class 1* — Explosives that must be expected to explode or detonate en masse very soon after fire reaches them. (92)
358. *Class 2* — Explosives that are readily ignited and burn with great violence without necessarily exploding. (92)
359. *Class 3* — Explosives that may explode en masse but, compared with Class 1 explosives, may be exposed to fire for some time before exploding. There will be a blast and fragment hazard. (92)
360. *Class 4* — Explosives that burn fiercely and give off dense smoke with toxic effects in some instances. There is no risk of mass explosion. (92)
361. *Class 5* — Explosives containing toxic substances. (92)
362. *Class 6* —Explosives that may be exposed to fire for some time before exploding. The risk of mass explosion is not involved, but small sporadic explosions occur with increasing frequency as the fire takes hold. There will be a fragment hazard but not a serious blast risk. (92)
363. *Class 7* — Explosives that involve combined flammable, toxic, and corrosive hazards. These may be exposed to fire for some time before exploding. The risk of mass explosion is not involved but explosions will occur with increasing frequency as the fire takes hold. There will be a fragment hazard arising from the pressure bursts but not a serious blast risk. (92)
364. *Class 8* — Explosives in which a radiological hazard is combined with an explosive hazard. (92)
365. *Class MP* — Substance containing metallic powders, such as magnesium, aluminum, or zinc powders, either in ammunition or in bulk facility storage. (92)

Hazardous Material	ID No.	Guide No.
366. Lead arsenite	*1618*	53
367. Flammable pesticide	*3021*	28
368. *Enamel*	1263	26
369. Gasoline	*1203*	27
370. *Sodium nitrate*	1498	35
371. *Aviation fuel*	1863	39
372. Tear gas	*1693*	58
373. Turpentine	*1299*	27
374. *Ammonium nitrate fertilizer*	2067	43
375. Fissile radioactive material	*2918*	63 (*ERG*)

LISTING

376. A. Shipper's name and address
    B. Receiver's name and address
    C. Proper shipping names of materials
    D. Hazard class of materials
    E. Identification number (UN/NA number)
    F. Packing group (in Roman numerals)
    G. Gross weight or volume shipped
    H. First-listed order of hazardous materials on shipping papers
    I. "X" or "RQ" before shipping name in "HM" column
    J. Emergency response telephone number (73, Table 3.5)

377. Answer should include at least one of each of those examples below from Table 3.4, or may include other appropriate examples approved by the instructor:
    A. *1.1* — Black powder
    B. *1.2* — Detonating cord
    C. *1.3* — Propellant explosives
    D. *1.4* — Practice ammunition
    E. *1.5* — Prilled ammonium nitrate
    F. *1.6* — Fertilizer fuel oil mixtures
    G. *2.1* — Propane
    H. *2.2* — Anhydrous ammonia
    I. *2.3* — Phosgene
    J. *3*   — Gasoline, kerosene, or diesel fuel
    K. *4.1* — Magnesium
    L. *4.2* — Phosphorus
    M. *4.3* — Calcium carbide
    N. *5.1* — Ammonium nitrate
    O. *5.2* — Ethyl ketone peroxide
    P. *6.1* — Arsenic
    Q. *6.2* — Rabies, HIV, Hepatitis B
    R. *7*   — Cobalt
    S. *8*   — Sulfuric acid, sodium hydroxide
    T. *9.1* — PCB, molten sulfur
    U. *9.2* — PCB, asbestos

3

    V. *9.3 —* Fumaric acid

    W. *ORM-D —* Consumer commodities (64, Table 3.4)

378. A. Verbal reports of bystanders or responsible persons on-site
    B. Occupancy type
    C. Incident location
    D. Trade and common names (40)

379. Answer should include any six of the following questions:
    A. Who are the reporting parties, and how did they get the information?
    B. What materials are involved, and how did the party identify them?
    C. How much material is involved, exposed, spilled, or leaking?
    D. Is the material leaking from a vessel or escaping under pressure?
    E. What is the estimated flow rate?
    F. Is it a static or flowing spill?
    G. Are sealed containers subject to the physical damage of fire exposure?
    H. What is the number, location, and condition of personnel needing rescue?
    I. Is any other information pertinent or peculiar to the situation? (40)

380. Answer should include any five of the following locations, but may include other appropriate examples approved by the instructor:
    A. Fuel storage facilities
    B. Paint supply stores
    C. Plant nurseries
    D. Doctors' and dentists' offices
    E. Photo processing laboratories
    F. Dry cleaners
    G. Plastic and high-technology factories
    H. Metal-plating businesses
    I. Mercantile concerns
    J. Automotive body shops (40, 41)

381. Answer should include any three examples under each of the transportation modes:
    A. *Highways* (41)
- Designated truck routes
- Blind intersections
- Poorly marked or poorly engineered interchanges
- Areas frequently congested by traffic
- Heavily traveled roads
- Sharp turns
- Steep grades
- Highway interchanges and ramps

    B. *Railways* (42)
- Depots, terminals, and switch or classification yards
- Sections of poorly laid or poorly maintained track
- Steep grades and severe curves
- Shunts and sidings
- Uncontrolled crossings

    C. *Water* (42)
- Difficult passages at bends or other threats to navigation
- Bridges and other crossings

- Piers and docks
- Shallows
- Locks
- Loading stations

D. *Air* (42)
- Fueling ramps
- Repair and maintenance hangars
- Freight terminals

E. *Pipeline* (42)
- Exposed crossings over waterways or roads
- Pumping stations
- Construction and demolition sites
- Intermediate or final storage facilities

382. A. To identify scene conditions from a distant location
   B. To assess and reevaluate the situation
   C. To complete donning protective clothing and respiratory protection
   D. To report any unusual conditions to the communications center
   E. To serve as a temporary staging area if reconnaissance teams must approach on foot (43)

383. Answer should include any four examples from each of the following actions/reactions:

A. *Physical actions* (44)
- Rainbow sheen on water surfaces
- Wavy vapors over a volatile liquid
- Frost near a leak
- Containers deformed by the force of an accident
- Operation of pressure-relief devices
- Pinging or popping of heat-exposed vessels

B. *Chemical reactions* (44)
- Extraordinary fire conditions
- Peeling or discoloration of a container's finish
- Spattering or boiling of unheated materials
- Distinctively colored vapor cloud
- Smoking or self-igniting materials
- Unexpected deterioration of equipment
- Peculiar smells
- Unexplained changes in ordinary materials
- Symptoms of chemical exposure

384. A. DOT *Emergency Response Guidebook (ERG)*
   B. *Dangerous Goods Guide to Initial Emergency Response (IERG)*
   C. Shipper's Emergency Response Center
   D. CHEMTREC/CANUTEC
   E. Material Safety Data Sheets (MSDS)(45)

385. A. Name of the caller and a call-back number
   B. Location of the incident
   C. Names of the material, shipper, and manufacturer
   D. Type of container or vehicle
   E. Railcar or truck number

3

      F. Carrier's name

      G. Consignee (material destination)

      H. Local conditions

      I. Action already taken (50)

386. A. Not every chemical manufacturer provides data to these organizations.

      B. The relevance of information these sources provide can only be as good as the information that first responders relay to the system.

      C. Much of the tactical information is general; the system will not make decisions for the incident commander.

      D. These systems are not infallible. (51)

387. Answer should include any four of the following associations, but may include other appropriate examples approved by the instructor:

      A. National Agricultural Chemical Association (NACA)

      B. Fertilizer Institute

      C. LP-Gas Association

      D. Chlorine Institute (51)

      E. Compressed Gas Association (CGA) (51)

388. A. *CHEMTREC* 1-800-424-9300 (51)

      B. *CANUTEC* 1-613-996-6666 (51)

389. A. *Section I* — Identification of manufacturer (51)

      B. *Section II* — Hazardous ingredients (51)

      C. *Section III* — Physical and chemical data (51)

      D. *Section IV* — Fire and explosion hazard data (51)

      E. *Section V* — Reactivity data (51)

      F. *Section VI* — Health hazard data (54)

      G. *Section VII* — Precautions for safe handling and use (54)

      H. *Section VIII* — Control measures (54)

390. Answer should include any three pieces of information in each of the following sections:

Section I (51)

      A. Manufacturer's name and address

      B. Emergency telephone number

      C. Information telephone number

      D. Signature and date

Section II (51)

      A. Common name

      B. Chemical name

      C. CAS number

      D. OSHA Permissible Exposure Limit (PEL)

      E. ACGIH Threshold Limit Value (TLV)

      F. Other Exposure Limits

Section III (51)

      A. Boiling point

      B. Specific gravity

      C. Vapor pressure

      D. Melting point

      E. Vapor density

      F. Evaporation rate

3

    G. Solubility in water

    H. Appearance and odor

Section IV (51)

    A. Flash point

    B. Flammable limits (LEL, UEL)

    C. Extinguishing media

    D. Special fire fighting procedures

    E. Unusual fire and explosion hazards

Section V (51)

    A. Stability (stable/unstable conditions to avoid)

    B. Incompatibility (materials to avoid)

    C. Hazardous decomposition or by-products

    D. Hazardous polymerization (may or may not occur, conditions to avoid)

Section VI (54)

    A. Routes of entry

    B. Health hazards (acute or chronic)

    C. Carcinogenicity

    D. NTP (National Toxicological Program)

    E. IARC (International Agency for Research on Cancer) monographs

    F. OSHA regulated

    G. Signs and symptoms of exposure

    H. Medical conditions aggravated by exposure

    I. Emergency and first aid procedures

Section VII (54)

    A. Steps to be taken in case material has been released or spilled

    B. Waste disposal methods

    C. Handling and storing precautions

    D. Other precautions

Section VIII (54)

    A. Respiratory protection

    B. Ventilation (local, mechanical, special, other)

    C. Protective gloves

    D. Eye protection

    E. Other protective clothing or equipment

    F. Work/hygienic practices

391. A. Miscellaneous Dangerous Goods

    B. Environmental Hazard

    C. Dangerous Waste (72)

392. A. Shipping papers

    B. Marking

    C. Labels

    D. Placards (72)

393. A. Proper shipping name of the material

    B. Hazard class represented by the material

    C. Packing group assigned to the material

    D. Quantity of the material (73)

3

394. Answer may include the following two examples, but may include other appropriate examples approved by the instructor:
    A. Cryogenic-liquid tank containers
    B. Tube model high-pressure cylinders (89)
395. A. Recognition of pressure/nonpressure cars
    B. Recognition of "dedicated" cars
    C. Stenciled material names
    D. Material packaging
    E. Construction features and color codings (83)
396. Answer should include any five of the following types of packaging:
    A. Drums
    B. Carboys
    C. Boxes
    D. Bottles
    E. Bags
    F. Wooden or cardboard barrels
    G. Portable tanks and bins (90)
397. A. Spring-loaded valves
    B. Heat-fusible plugs
    C. Pressure-activated bursting discs (90)
398. Answer should include any five of the following pieces of label information:
    A. The words EXTREMELY FLAMMABLE
    B. EPA registration number (if originating in U.S.)
    C. PCP Number (if originating in Canada)
    D. Mode of entry into body
    E. Requirements for storage and disposal
    F. First aid information
    G. Antidote for poisoning if known (92, 93)
399. A. Combustible-gas or explosive meters
    B. Oxygen meters
    C. Toxicity monitoring devices (94)

LABELING

400. A. Health rating
    B. Flammability hazard
    C. Reactivity hazard
    D. Special hazard (56)
401. A. Hazard
    B. Class
    C. UN number
    D. Packing group
    E. Weight (73)
402. A. Colored background
    B. Hazard class symbol
    C. Four-digit identification number
    D. UN hazard class number (65-67)

403. A. Reporting marks (initials)
    B. Tank number
    C. Country code
    D. Size/type code (88)
404. A. Warning
    B. Product
    C. Emergency phone number
    D. Product owner (93)

SHORT ANSWER

405. A. Prepare pre-incident plans
    B. Establish procedures
    C. Tentatively preassign actions (39)
406. A. Location and quantities of hazardous materials in the area
    B. Dangers of the hazardous materials
    C. Possible difficulties of property access
    D. Inherent limitations of the department to control certain types of haz mat emergencies (39)
407. *Hazardous Materials Emergency Planning Guide* (NRT-1) from the National Response Team (39)
408. Materials may have been transferred from their original, labeled containers; dangerous substances may have been hidden to avoid detection by chance inspection. (41)
409. A. *Changes in respiration* — Difficult breathing, increase or decrease in respiration rate, tightness of the chest, irritation of the nose and throat, and/or respiratory arrest
    B. *Changes in consciousness* — Dizziness, lightheadedness, drowsiness, confusion, fainting, and/or unconsciousness
    C. *Abdominal distress* — Nausea, vomiting, and/or cramping
    D. *Change in activity level* — Fatigue, weakness, stupor, hyperactivity, restlessness, anxiety, giddiness, and/or faulty judgment
    E. *Visual disturbances* — Double vision, blurred vision, cloudy vision, burning of the eyes, and/or dilated or constricted pupils
    F. *Skin changes* — Burning sensations, reddening, paleness, fever, and/or chills
    G. *Changes in excretion or thirst* — Uncontrolled tears, profuse sweating, mucus flowing from the nose, diarrhea, frequent urination, bloody stool, and/or intense thirst
    H. *Pain* — Headache, muscle ache, stomach ache, chest pain, and/or localized pain at sites of substance contact (44)
410. The *IERG* and *ERG* placarding and labeling systems are similar and reciprocal, but *IERG*'s contains additional or different placards for corrosive gas, miscellaneous dangerous goods, and dangerous wastes. (45-49)
411. Description should include the following information:
    Provides signal or alert to first responders that hazardous materials are present; identifies the general hazards and the degree of severity for health, flammability, and reactivity; provides immediate information necessary to protect the lives of both the public and emergency response personnel (55, 56)

3

412. Recognition of the type of container; identification of the material in the container; transmission of this information to an appropriate authority (57)

413. Marking regulations are designed to provide first responders with a method of identifying a haz mat package or container in the event that it becomes separated from its associated shipping papers. (75)

414. A. *Markings* provide information on the contents and qualifications of the packaging used, and include the following information: proper shipping name, UN/NA ID number, name and address of consignee.
   B. *Labels* are usually small replicas of vehicle placards; they may or may not contain written text.
   C. *Placards* are 10¾-inch square, on-point diamond shaped signs containing a pictogram and hazard class or division number indicating the hazards represented by the materials contained within the packaging or conveyance. (75)

415. The name of the material is printed on the car and the manufacturer's name or logo may also be printed on the car. Also, some dedicated cars are a distinctive color — which is determined by the owner and is not subject to regulation. (85)

416. They usually have visible fittings or an expansion dome. (84)

417. They are usually smaller because of the density and weight of the materials, they generally have no plumbing underneath because they are loaded and unloaded from the top, and they may have a protective black band around the car under the dome area. (84)

418. A. *Maximum capacity (liquid)* — 119 gallons (450 L)
   B. *Maximum net mass (solid)* — 882 pounds (400 kg)
   C. *Maximum capacity (in gallons/liters) as a receptacle for a solid* — 119 gallons (450 L)
   D. *Liquid capacity (in pounds/kilograms) as a receptacle for a gas* — Greater than 1,000 pounds (454 kg) (90)

419. Nearly all military ordnance are designed to inflict great bodily harm or heavy property damage; military drivers may be under orders not to identify their cargoes. (91)

420. A. *DANGER/POISON* — Highly toxic materials
   B. *WARNING* — Moderately toxic materials
   C. *CAUTION* — Relatively low toxicity (92)

4

Chapter 4 Answers

DEFINITIONS OF KEY TERMS

1. *Ballistic* — Like a bullet or projectile. (Dict.)
2. *Breach* — A container that is stressed beyond its limits of recovery (its design strength and ability to hold contents) and thus opens up. (102)
3. *Deflagration* — Chemical reaction producing vigorous heat and sparks or flame and moving through the material (as black or smokeless powder) at less than the

speed of sound; can also refer to intense burning; a characteristic of Class B explosives. (106, xvi)

4. *Divert* — To turn from one course or path to another. (Dict.)
5. *Engulf* — In GEBMO, the dispersion of material; generally, the engulfing event is when matter and/or energy disperses forming a danger zone. (104)
6. *Harm* — Injury or damage caused by exposure to a hazardous material. (106)
7. *Impingement* — Come into sharp contact with. (105)
8. *Mitigation* — Actions taken to lessen the harm or hostile nature of an incident. (97)
9. *Polymerization* — Reaction (often violent) in which two or more molecules chemically combine to form larger molecules. (101, xxv)
10. *Strategy* — A plan or method for accomplishing a goal. (Dict.)
11. *Stress* — Stimulus causing strain (excessive tension or compression), pressure (force applied at right angles to a surface), or deformity (distortion by torque or twisting). (102)

TRUE/FALSE

12. False. First responders can identify *but generally will need help from more highly trained personnel to achieve completion of a primary objective.* (97)
13. False. The factor that most affects all areas of response is the *hazardous material.* (99)
14. True (103)
15. True (101)
16. False. Usually there will be *more than one way to achieve an objective, each must be analyzed and the desired alternative(s) selected.* (101)
17. True (98)
18. False. Detonation is best defined as *the instantaneous and explosive release of the stored chemical energy of a hazardous material.* (103)
19. True (103)

MATCHING

20. B
21. C
22. A (102)

23. A
24. C
25. B (99)

IDENTIFICATION

26. *Footprint* — The outline of a dispersing hazardous material (104)
27. *GEBMO* — General Emergency Behavior Model; a defensive-mode action concerned with potential haz mat container emergencies (101)
28. *Immediate concern tasks* — Preventive measures that can be performed by the first responder and can be carried out with minimal or no risk to the first responder (97)

4

29. *Primary objective* — Specific goal-oriented tasks that will bring the incident to an end (98)

30. *Strategic objective* — General objective relating to the standard goals of emergency response (99)

31. A. *D*etect haz mat presence.
    B. *E*stimate likely harm without intervention.
    C. *C*hoose response objectives.
    D. *I*dentify action options.
    E. *D*o best option.
    F. *E*valuate progress. (97, Table 4.1)

32. A. *I*dentify the nature of the problem.
    B. *F*ormulate objectives based on the available information and resources.
    C. *S*elect the desired alternative(s) from the available options.
    D. *T*ake appropriate action.
    E. *A*nalyze outcomes continually. (100)

33. A. Cone (105)
    B. Plume (105)
    C. Pool (106)
    D. Hemispheric or dome-shaped (104)
    E. Stream (106)
    F. Cloud (105)

LISTING

34. Answer should include any five of the following examples:
    A. Isolating the area
    B. Denying access to the area
    C. Evacuating or sheltering in place
    D. Diking and retaining the spill in a specific area for collection
    E. Diverting liquid and runoff water into an isolated location to control the speed of contamination
    F. Eliminating all ignition sources within an appropriate distance
    G. Cooling tanks involved in fire or exposed to heat by accepted methods to reduce the probability of rupture (98)

35. Answer should include any three of the following examples:
    A. Extinguishing fires and stabilizing the scene
    B. Controlling flammable and/or toxic gas clouds
    C. Stopping leaks by plugging and/or patching
    D. Diking and damming large-volume spills (98)

36. Answer should include any four of the following factors:
    A. Location and severity of the incident
    B. Properties of the involved material(s)
    C. Size and extent of the incident
    D. Damage sustained by containers
    E. Availability of resources to handle the incident
    F. Limitations of the first responders
    G. Accuracy of tactics applied (98, 99)

37. A. Their ability to be achieved
    B. Their ability to prevent further injuries and/or deaths
    C. Their ability to minimize environmental and property damage within the constraints of safety, time, equipment, and personnel (99)
38. Answer should include any two of the following actions:
    A. Setting and achieving immediate goals and objectives
    B. Knowing or estimating the resources required for the situation
    C. Managing personnel, equipment, and resources to solve the problem (100)
39. Answer should include any seven of the following questions:
    A. Where is the incident scene in relation to population and environmental and property exposures?
    B. What are the hazardous materials?
    C. What hazard classes are involved?
    D. What quantities are involved?
    E. How could the material react?
    F. Is it a liquid or solid spill or a gas release?
    G. Is something burning?
    H. What kind of container holds the material?
    I. What is the condition of the container?
    J. How much time has elapsed since the incident began?
    K. What personnel, equipment, and extinguishing agents are available?
    L. Is there private fire protection or other help available?
    M. What effect can the weather have?
    N. What has already been done? (100)
40. A. How long will the harmful exposure last?
    B. What has stressed or is stressing the container?
    C. How will the stressed container and its material behave?
    D. What are the effects of the container materials? (101, 102)
41. A. Stress (Identify the types of stress.)
    B. Breach (Predict the type of breach.)
    C. Release (Predict the type of release.)
    D. Engulf (Predict the dispersion pattern.)
    E. Contact (Predict the length of exposure.)
    F. Harm (Predict the hazard causing the harm.) (97, Table 4.1)
42. A. Thermal
    B Chemical
    C. Mechanical (102)
43. Answer should be ranked in the following order:
    A. Detonation
    B. Violent rupture
    C. Rapid relief
    D. Spill/leak (103)
44. A. Timing of release (speed at which material escapes or length of exposure)
    B. Size of area covered by release
    C. Toxicity (relative level of harm) (106)

4

45. The first responder may address immediate concern tasks by predicting a possible explosion or by deciding to let the fire burn to consume the hazardous material involved. (98)

46. The incident commander's primary concerns must be to 1) influence the incident favorably with available resources, 2) go into a temporary holding action, or 3) withdraw all personnel to safety if necessary. (99)

47. A. Initiating the conclusion of the immediate haz mat emergency
    B. Ensuring the termination of the haz mat emergency
    C. Avoiding the creation of any new problems (101)

48. A. Detonation is an instantaneous, explosive release that may include fragmentation, disintegration, or shattering of container; extreme overpressure; and considerable heat release.
    B. Violent rupture is the immediate release of chemical or mechanical energy caused by runaway cracks; may result in ballistic behavior of container and its contents.
    C. Rapid relief is the fast release of a pressurized hazardous material through safety devices; damaged valves, piping, or attachments; or through holes in the container.
    D. Spill/leak is the slow release of a hazardous material under atmospheric or head pressure through holes, rips, tears, or ordinary openings/attachments in container. (103)

49. Answer may include any one of the examples listed for each breach, or may include other examples approved by the instructor.
    A. *Disintegration* — Glass bottle shattering; grenade exploding
    B. *Runaway cracking* — Drum, tank, carboy cracking
    C. *Attachments (closures) opening up* — Pressure relief valve or discharge valve breaking off container
    D. *Puncture* — Forklift puncturing drum; coupler puncturing rail tank car
    E. *Split or tear* — Welded seam on tank; ripped seam on bag of fertilizer (103)

50. Answer may include any one of the following examples for each duration, or may include other examples approved by the instructor:
    A. *Immediate* — Deflagration, explosion, detonation
    B. *Short term* — Gas cloud, vapor cloud
    C. *Medium term* — Lingering pesticide
    D. *Long term* — Permanent radioactive source (106)

5

Chapter 5 Answers

1. *Cryogenic* — Cooled to a very low temperature. (113, xvi)
2. *Catalyst* — Substance that modifies (usually increases) the rate of chemical reaction without being consumed in the process. (117, Dict.)
3. *Dedicated* — Given over to a particular purpose. (111)

4. *Encapsulating* — Completely enclosed or surrounded as in a capsule. (109, Dict.)
5. *Leach* — To pass out or through by percolation (gradual seepage). (111)
6. *Nullify* — To cancel or make void. (115, Dict.)
7. *Permeate* — To diffuse through or penetrate something. (110, Dict.)
8. *Proximity* — In the area of; very near; close. (113, Dict.)
9. *Sorbent* — Granular, porous filtering material used in vapor- and gas-removing respirators. (117)
10. *Sorption* — Method of removing contaminants; used in vapor- and gas-removing respirators. (117)
11. *Untethered* — Free from restraints; not connected by airline to a fixed air source. (116, Dict.)

TRUE/FALSE

12. False. High-temperature protective clothing offers *very limited* protection against chemical hazards. (113)
13. False. Level A protective equipment is a *vapor-protective encapsulating suit.* (109)
14. True (109)
15. False. *There is no single combination of protective equipment that can protect against all hazards.* (109)
16. True (111)
17. True (111)
18. True (111)
19. True (111)
20. False. Vapor-protective suits are primarily used as part of a *Level A* protective ensemble. (112)
21. False. Support-function protective garments are worn by personnel working *outside* the hot zone. (113)
22. True (113)
23. False. Chemical protective clothing *should be* used in conjunction with any other protective equipment required by the situation. (111)
24. True (113)
25. False. *Open-circuit SCBA* are the most commonly used protective breathing apparatus in the fire service. (114)
26. False. The air supply in open-circuit SCBA is *compressed breathing air.* (114)
27. False. Most SCBA allow *at least 15 to 20 minutes* of heavy work to be performed. (115)
28. False. NFPA and ANSI standards require that only *positive-pressure* breathing apparatus be used in the fire service. (115)
29. True (115)
30. True (118)
31. False. Air-purifying respirators *cannot* be worn in oxygen-deficient atmospheres. (117)
32. True (120)
33. True (120)

5

34. C (111)
35. D (111)
36. A (114)
37. B (116, 117)
38. A (117)
39. D (117)

40. C
41. B
42. A (113)

43. National Institute of Occupational Safety and Health (109)
44. United States Coast Guard (109)
45. Environmental Protection Agency (109)
46. Mine Safety and Health Administration (115)
47. *Emergency Response Guidebook* (U.S.) (120)
48. *Dangerous Goods Guide to Initial Emergency Response* (Canada) (120)
49. National Fire Protection Association's *Hazardous Chemical Data* (109, 110)
50. National Fire Protection Association's *Standard on Vapor-Protective Suits for Hazardous Chemical Emergencies* (112)
51. National Fire Protection Association's *Standard on Liquid Splash-Protective Suits for Hazardous Chemical Emergencies* (112)
52. National Fire Protection Association's *Standard on Support Function Protective Garments for Hazardous Chemical Operations* (113)
53. National Fire Protection Association's *Professional Competence of Responders to Hazardous Materials Incidents (109)*
54. Occupational Safety and Health Administration Code of Federal Regulations (119)

55. C
56. B
57. D
58. A
59. C
60. B
61. C
62. D
63. B
64. A (109)

5

65. A. Helmet
   B. SCBA
   C. Turnout coat and pants
   D. Protective boots
   E. Protective hood
   F. Gloves (110)
66. Answer should contain any three of the following limitations:
   A. Not corrosive resistant; therefore, acids and bases can dissolve outer layers.
   B. Not vapor tight; therefore, gases can penetrate garment.
   C. Gaps occur at neck, wrists, waist, and the point where the pants and boots overlap.
   D. Hazardous materials can permeate and remain in the equipment, subjecting the wearer to repeated exposure or a later reaction with another chemical. (110)
67. Answer should contain any two of the following limitations:
   A. Clothing does not provide protection against all chemicals.
   B. Limited-use garments cannot be reused if contaminated.
   C. Reusable garments can retain some chemicals at the molecular level that may leach out later and pose a hazard to the wearer. (111)
68. A. Chemical cartridge
   B. Gas mask
   C. Particulate-vapor and gas-removing (117)
69. Answer should contain any five of the following conditions:
   A. Asthma
   B. Emphysema
   C. Chronic lung disease
   D. Psychological problems or symptoms including claustrophobia
   E. Physical deformities or abnormalities of the face
   F. Medication use
   G. Intolerance to increased heart rate, which can be produced by heat stress (119)
70. Answer should contain any five of the following equipment limitations:
   A. Limited visibility
   B. Decreased ability to communicate — The facepiece hinders voice communication
   C. Increased weight
   D. Decreased mobility
   E. Inadequate oxygen levels (air-purifying respirators cannot be worn in IDLH or oxygen-deficient atmospheres)
   F. Chemical specific (air-purifying respirators protect only against certain chemicals) (119,120)
71. Answer should contain any five of the following air supply limitations:
   A. Physical condition of user
   B. Degree of physical exertion
   C. Emotional stability
   D. Condition of apparatus
   E. Cylinder pressure before use
   F. Training and experience (120)

5

72. A. *Chlordane* — Positive-pressure SCBA and chemical protective clothing specifically recommended by the shipper or manufacturer (it will provide little or no thermal protection); structural firefighter protective clothing is ***not*** effective for this material. (1993 *ERG*, Guide 28)
  B. *Flammable solid (3178)* — Positive-pressure SCBA and structural firefighter's protective clothing will provide ***limited*** protection. (1993 *ERG*, Guide 32)
  C. *Uranium nitrate hexahydrate solution* — Positive-pressure SCBA and structural firefighter's protective clothing will provide ***adequate*** protection. (1993 *ERG*, Guide 61)
  D. *Molten aluminum* — Positive-pressure SCBA and flame-retardant structural firefighter's protective clothing, including faceshield, helmet, and gloves, will provide ***limited*** thermal protection. (1993 *ERG*, Guide 77)
  E. *Radioactive material (2974)* — Positive-pressure SCBA and structural firefighter's protective clothing will provide ***adequate*** protection against internal radiation exposure, but ***not*** against external exposure. (1993 *ERG*, Guide 64)
  F. *Fissile uranium hexafluoride* — Positive-pressure SCBA and chemical-protective clothing specifically recommended by the shipper or manufacturer; structural firefighter's protective clothing will ***not*** provide protection from vapors. (1993 *ERG*, Guide 66)
  G. *Refrigerated liquid hydrogen* — Positive-pressure SCBA and structural firefighter's protective clothing will provide ***limited*** protection. (1993 *ERG*, Guide 22)
  H. *Anhydrous ammonia* — Positive-pressure SCBA and chemical-protective clothing specifically recommended by the shipper or manufacturer (it will provide little or no thermal protection); structural firefighter's protective clothing is ***not*** effective for this material. (1993 *ERG*, Guide 15)
  I. *Asbestos* — Positive-pressure SCBA and structural firefighter's protective clothing will provide ***limited*** protection. (1992 *ERG*, Guide 31)

73. A. *Acrolein (uninhibited)*
  - *Guide — 30*
  - *Health hazards*
    — Poisonous; may be fatal if inhaled, swallowed, or absorbed through the skin.
    — Contact may cause burns to skin and eyes.
    — Runoff from fire control or dilution water may cause pollution.
  B. *Vinyl butyl ether*
  - *Guide — 26*
  - *Health hazards*
    — May be poisonous if inhaled or absorbed through the skin.
    — Vapors may cause dizziness or suffocation.
    — Contact may irritate or burn skin and eyes.
    — Fire may produce irritating or poisonous gases.
    — Runoff from fire control or dilution water may give off poisonous gases and cause water pollution.
  C. *Petroleum naptha*
  - *Guide — 27*
  - *Health hazards*

5

    — May be poisonous if inhaled or absorbed through the skin.
    — Vapors may cause dizziness or suffocation.
    — Contact may irritate or burn skin and eyes.
    — Fire may produce irritating or poisonous gases.
    — Runoff from fire control or dilution water may cause pollution.

D. *Methyl chloride*
  - *Guide* — 18
  - *Health hazards*
    - Poisonous; may be fatal if inhaled, swallowed, or absorbed through the skin.
    - Contact causes burns to skin and eyes.
    - Contact with liquid may cause frostbite.
    - Runoff from fire control or dilution water may cause pollution.

E. *Hydrochloric acid solution*
  - *Guide* — 60
  - *Health hazards*
    - Contact causes burns to skin and eyes.
    - If inhaled, may be harmful.
    - Fire may produce irritating or poisonous gases.
    - Runoff from fire control or dilution water may cause pollution.

F. *Refrigerated (cryogenic) liquid helium*
  - *Guide* — 21
  - *Health hazards*
    - Vapors may cause dizziness or suffocation.
    - Contact with liquid may cause frostbite.

G. *Asbestos*
  - *Guide* — 31
  - *Health hazards*
    - Contact may cause burns to skin and eyes.
    - Inhalation of asbestos dust may have damaging effect on lungs.
    - Fire may produce irritating or poisonous gases.
    - Runoff from fire control or dilution water may cause pollution.

H. *LOX*
  - *Guide* — 23
  - *Health hazards*
    - Vapors may cause dizziness or suffocation.
    - Contact will cause severe frostbite.
    - Fire may produce irritating or poisonous gases.

SHORT ANSWER

74. A. *Egress cylinder* — This small compressed air cylinder is intended to provide enough breathing air (about 5 minutes) to allow the wearer of airline breathing equipment to escape the atmosphere in the event that the airline is severed. These cylinders *should not* be used for untethered work. (117)

    B. *Closed-circuit cylinder* — This small cylinder contains pure oxygen and allows the wearer of closed-circuit SCBA 30 minutes to 4 hours of air for untethered work. (117, 118)

5

75. A. *Physical condition* — The wearer must be in sound physical condition in order to maximize the work that can be performed and to stretch the air supply (both open- and closed-circuit types) as far as possible. (118)
    B. *Agility* — Wearing a protective breathing apparatus with an air cylinder or backpack restricts the wearer's movements and affects his or her balance. Good agility will overcome these obstacles. (118)
    C. *Facial features* — The shape and contour of the face will affect the wearer's ability to get a good facepiece-to-face seal. (118)
    D. *Neurological functioning* — Good motor coordination is necessary for operating in protective breathing equipment. First responders must be of sound mind to handle emergency situations that arise. (118)
    E. *Muscular/skeletal condition* — The first responder must have the physical strength and size required to wear the protective equipment and to perform necessary tasks. (118)
    F. *Cardiovascular conditioning* — Poor cardiovascular conditioning can result in heart attacks, strokes, or other related problems during strenuous activity. (118)
    G. *Respiratory functioning* — Proper respiratory functioning will maximize the wearer's operation time in a self-contained breathing apparatus. (119)
    H. *Training in equipment use* — The first responder must be knowledgeable in every aspect of protective breathing apparatus use. (119)
    I. *Self-confidence* — The first responder's belief in his or her ability will have an extremely positive overall effect on the actions that are performed. (119)
    J. *Emotional stability* — The ability to maintain control in an excited or high-stress environment will reduce the chances of a serious mistake being made. (119)

6

Chapter 6 Answers

DEFINITIONS OF KEY TERMS

1. *Estuary* — An arm of the sea at the lower end of a river. (139, Dict.)
2. *Utilidor* — An insulated, heated conduit built below the ground surface or supported above the ground surface to protect the contained water, steam, sewage, and fire lines from freezing. (139, xxviii)

TRUE/FALSE

3. True (125)
4. True (125)
5. False. *Because written copies of LERPs are too bulky to be easily used on a response,* first responders should carry a *checklist of the initial actions to be taken.* (126)
6. True (126)
7. True (127)
8. False. Dispatchers *should* be included in responder training sessions and exercises. (127)
9. False. Internal communication begins when *emergency personnel arrive at the scene.* (127)

10. False. Dispatchers *must not filter, edit, delete, or change the information that they receive.* (127)
11. True (127)
12. True. *(When direct communication with technical advisors is not possible, the dispatcher must perform the function of liasion between the technical advisor and on-scene personnel.)* (127)
13. False. Once the incident action plan is formulated, *the level of training of the first responder at the operational level will limit participation in the implementation of the plan.* (129)
14. False. The first person on the scene *or the ranking individual of the first company on the scene* assumes command of the incident *until a higher ranking or more extensively trained responder arrives on the scene and assumes command following a briefing.* (130, 131)
15. True. *(The IC may choose to delegate some of these functions to others.)* (131)
16. True (133)
17. False. A *Level I* incident is the least serious and the easiest to handle. (135)
18. True (141)
19. False. The Canadian *IERG* does not contain initial *isolation* distances. (141)
20. False. The smallest isolation distance given in the *ERG* for any chemical is *500 feet.* (141)
21. True (143)
22. False. Vehicles are *not as effective* as buildings for protection-in-place, *but they can offer temporary protection if the windows are closed and the ventilation system is turned off.* (143)
23. True (144)
24. False. It is considered *safe* for workers to enter the warm zone *briefly* without special protective clothing. (144)
25. True (145)
26. False. The command post *should* be located where the incident commander can observe the scene, *although such a location is not absolutely necessary.* (145)
27. False. First responders *should protect themselves in case a contaminated victim has not been thoroughly decontaminated.* (145)

MULTIPLE CHOICE

28. C (133)
29. D (141)
30. D (*ERG*, 141)
31. A (*ERG*, 141)
32. B (142)
33. C (*ERG*, 141)
34. B (143)

IDENTIFICATION

35. *External communication* — Initial receipt of information (126)
36. *Internal communication* — Information regarding the incident that is received when personnel arrive on the scene (126)

6

37. *Complaint* — Outside call to the dispatcher (126)
38. *Hazard assessment* — The continual mental process of considering all available factors that will immediately affect the incident during the course of the operation (132)
39. *Nonintervention operation* — Operation in which responders take no direct actions on the actual problem (133)
40. *Offensive operation* — Operation in which responders take aggressive, direct action on the material, container, or process equipment involved in the incident (134)
41. *Defensive operation* — Operation in which responders seek to confine the emergency to a given area, without directly contacting the materials causing the emergency (134)
42. *Level I incident* — Least serious and easiest to handle; within the capabilities of first responders at the awareness and operational levels (135)
43. *Level II incident* — Incident that is beyond the capabilities of the first responders on the scene and may be beyond the capabilities of the first response agency having jurisdiction; these incidents require the services of a formal haz mat response team (135)
44. *Level III incident* — The most serious of all haz mat incidents; requires resources from state agencies, federal agencies, and/or private industry and may require a large-scale evacuation (137)
45. *Topographical aspect* — The relative position of land features (139, Dict.)
46. *Evacuation* — Movement of people from a threatened area to a safer place (143)
47. *Protection-in-place* — The process of directing people to go quickly inside a building and to remain inside until the danger passes (143)
48. *Hot zone* — Area surrounding the incident that has been contaminated by the released material (144)
49. *Warm zone* — Area abutting the hot zone and extending to the cold zone (144)
50. *Cold zone* — Encompasses the warm zone and is used to carry out all other support functions of the incident (145)
51. *SARA* — Title III of the Superfund Amendments and Reauthorization Act (125)
52. *LERP* — Local emergency response plan (125)
53. *LEPC* — Local emergency planning committee (125)
54. *EMO* — Emergency measures organization (Canada's LERP) (125)
55. *SOP* — Standard operating procedure (126)
56. *ERG* — *Emergency Response Guidebook* (127)
57. *IERG* — *Initial Emergency Response Guide* (Canada) (127)
58. *IC* — Incident commander (131)
59. *OSHA 1910.120* — Occupational Safety and Health Administration regulations that include an explanation of the awareness and operational levels of haz mat response (128)
60. *NFPA 472* — National Fire Protection Association's *Professional Competence of Responders to Hazardous Materials Incidents* (122)
61. *NFPA 471* — National Fire Protection Association's *Recommended Practice for Responding to Hazardous Materials Incidents* (137)
62. *HVAC* — Heating, ventilating, and air-conditioning (143)
63. *IFSTA* — International Fire Service Training Association (143, iii)

64. A, D, G (128, 129)

65. A. II
    B. I
    C. III
    D. II
    E. II
    F. I
    G. I
    H. III
    I. I
    J. II
    K. III
    L. II
    M. II (135-137)

LISTING

66. A. Haz mat facilities and transportation routes
    B. Methods and procedures for handling haz mat incidents
    C. Methods to warn people at risk
    D. Haz mat equipment and information resources
    E. Evacuation plans
    F. Training of first responders
    G. Schedule for existing LERP (125)
67. Answer should include any ten of the following areas:
    A. Location of the incident
    B. Name, phone number, and location of the caller
    C. Identity of the substance involved (spelled out if possible)
    D. Approximate quantity of the material
    E. Type of container
    F. Condition of container
    G. Prevailing weather conditions
    H. Number and proximity of persons or properties
    I. Brief description of events leading to the incident
    J. Any obvious threatening effects of the hazardous material
    K. Summary of local actions taken or underway
    L. Type of assistance needed
    M. Arrangements for recontacting the reporting party (126)
68. Answer should include any three of the following responsibilities:
    A. Establishing internal or external clear-line communications with technical advisors
    B. Notifying mutual aid agencies
    C. Activating other prescribed departmental procedures
    D. Advising next-in-line supervisors and chief officers of the incident (127)
69. A. Establish defensive goals.
    B. Identify defensive tactical options to meet the goals.
    C. Ensure the appropriateness of the training and personal protective equipment of on-scene personnel for the actions to be taken.

6

    D. Prepare for emergency decontamination of contaminated responders or civilians. (129)

70. Answer should include any five of the following tasks:
    A. Establishing protective zones
    B. Activating the incident management system
    C. Using personal protective equipment
    D. Carrying out defensive activities
    E. Evaluating and reporting incident progress
    F. Performing emergency decontamination procedures (129)

71. A. Establishing the site safety plan
    B. Implementing a site security and controlling plan to limit the number of personnel operating in the control zone
    C. Designating a safety officer
    D. Identifying the materials or conditions involved in the incident
    E. Implementing appropriate emergency operations
    F. Ensuring that appropriate personal protective equipment is worn
    G. Establishing a decontamination plan and operation (131)

72. A. Maintain communications with the IC.
    B. Identify hazardous situations at the incident scene.
    C. Participate in incident planning.
    D. Review incident action plans for safety issues.
    E. Identify and immediately correct potentially unsafe situations if necessary. (131)

73. A. Nature of the call
    B. Location of the call
    C. Equipment responding
    D. Time of day
    E. Weather (132)

74. Answer should include any six of the following responsibilities:
    A. Evaluating response route
    B. Reviewing plans and sketches
    C. Noting arrival time of other responding units
    D. Noting exposure types and distances
    E. Reviewing hydrant and water supply conditions
    F. Considering access to the scene
    G. Making preliminary plans for apparatus placement at the scene
    H. Securing any additional information from the dispatcher
    I. Deciding if and what additional units are needed (132)

75. A. Unusual signs (smoke, fire, explosions, leaking material, vapor clouds, etc.)
    B. Life hazards
    C. Material(s) involved
    D. Path of fire or material travel
    E. Actions already taken by people on the scene (133)

76. A. The facility or LERP calls for the nonintervention mode based on a pre-incident evaluation of the hazards present at the site.
    B. The situation is clearly beyond the capabilities of responders.
    C. Explosions are imminent.
    D. Serious container damage threatens a massive release. (133, 134)

77. A. Withdraw to a safe distance.
     B. Report scene conditions to dispatch.
     C. Establish scene control.
     D. Initiate the incident management system.
     E. Initiate evacuation where needed.
     F. Call for additional resources. (134)
78. A. The facility or LERP calls for the defensive mode based on pre-incident evaluation of the hazards present at the site.
     B. The responders have the training and equipment necessary to confine the incident to the area of origin. (134)
79. Answer should contain any six of the following actions:
     A. Report scene conditions to dispatch.
     B. Establish scene control.
     C. Initiate the incident management system.
     D. Establish and indicate zone boundaries.
     E. Commence evacuation where needed.
     F. Control material spread by diverting it to a safe location.
     G. Construct dikes or dams to confine the materials.
     H. Control ignition sources.
     I. Call for additional resources. (134)
80. A. Extent of municipal, county, state, and federal involvement (or potential involvement)
     B. Level of technical expertise required at the scene
     C. Extent of evacuation of civilians
     D. Extent of injuries or deaths (135)
81. A. Using chemical clothing
     B. Diking and confining material within contaminated areas
     C. Plugging and patching
     D. Sampling and testing unknown substances
     E. Performing various levels of decontamination (135)
82. A. Specialists from industry and government agencies
     B. Sophisticated sampling and monitoring equipment
     C. Specialized leak and spill control techniques
     D. Decontamination on a large scale (137)
83. Answer should include any five of the following questions:
     A. Are the responders working as members of a team?
     B. Have all responders been adequately briefed on the incident action plan and the hazards of the situation?
     C. Can reconnaissance be made visually?
     D. Can approach be made from upwind/uphill?
     E. Can contact with the material be avoided?
     F. Can the vapor cloud, mist, dust, or smoke spread?
     G. Is the risk worth the benefit? (137)
84. A. The immediate goal
     B. Who performs each task
     C. Operation completion time
     D. How to call for help
     E. The escape route

6

    F. The material's effects

    G. Signs and symptoms of exposure (137)

85. A. Avoid contact with mists, vapors, dusts, and smoke.

    B. Maintain a safe distance, and stay outside the hot zone.

    C. Use available shielding, and stay with emergency vehicle if necessary.

    D. Anticipate change — such as delayed reactions by the material and weather conditions. (138)

86. A. Container integrity — Does the container show signs of failure?

    B. Safety devices — Is the container equipped with vents or relief devices? Are the vents or relief devices operating properly?

    C. Leaking — Are seals, gaskets, and connections still intact?

    D. Stability — Is the container likely to move? (139)

87. Answer should include any two of the following methods:

    A. Siren signal

    B. Air horn signal

    C. Emergency radio broadcast (139)

88. A. Internal combustion engines

    B. Electric motors, switches, and controllers

    C. Lighting equipment

    D. Fuel-powered equipment

    E. Open or pilot flames

    F. Electrostatic or frictional sparks

    G. Heated metal surfaces

    H. Smoking materials

    I. Fuses, flares, torpedoes, and lanterns

    J. Radios, hand lights, pagers, and PASS devices (140)

89. Answer should include any five of the following ways:

    A. Station a responder at approaches and refuse entry.

    B. Activate local alarm devices.

    C. Reroute traffic away from the scene.

    D. Put up physical barriers — tape, rope, or barricades.

    E. Transmit warnings over a public address system.

    F. Broadcast an alert via the media.

    G. Stage responders an adequate distance away. (141, 142)

90. A. Decontaminate evacuees if necessary.

    B. Record evacuees' identities.

    C. Perform triage or give treatment. (142)

91. Answer should include any three of the following guidelines:

    A. The population is unable to initiate evacuation because of health care, detention, or educational occupancies.

    B. The material is spreading too rapidly.

    C. The material is too toxic to risk exposure.

    D. Vapors are heavier than air, and the people are in a high-rise structure. (143)

92. Answer must be listed in the order below:

    A. Identify the material name and ID number.

    B. Find the corresponding name and ID number in the green *ERG* or yellow *IERG* pages.

    C. Size the spill by container or amount.

6

    D. Take the distance from the *Table of Initial Isolation and Protective Action Distance* in the *ERG*.

    E. Apply the appropriate protective action.

    F. Seek additional information in the *ERG/IERG* 2-digit guide pages. (143)

93. A. Predetermined location at a facility
    B. Conveniently located building
    C. Radio-equipped vehicle located in the cold zone (145)

94. Answer may include any three of the following examples, but may include other appropriate examples approved by the instructor:
    A. Green flashing light
    B. Pennants
    C. Signs
    D. Flags (145)

LABELING

95. A. Hazard area
    B. Hot zone
    C. Warm zone
    D. Cold zone
    E. Haz mat control officer
    F. Forward access point
    G. Decontamination area
    H. Safe haven
    I. Staging area (equipment cache)
    J. Command post (144)

SHORT ANSWER

96. Requires jurisdictions in the United States to develop a local emergency response plan for haz mat incidents (125)

97. A. *Common terminology* — Names of organizational elements, resources, and facilities should be consistent.
    B. *Modular organization* — The management system should be built from the top down, with branches/sections added as needed according to the size and complexity of the incident.
    C. *Integrated communication* — All of the agencies involved in the incident must be able to communicate with each other.
    D. *Unified command structure* — All of the individuals or agencies that have jurisdictional responsibility should be represented within the command structure. (130)

98. Answer must be listed in the order below:
    A. Life safety
    B. Environmental protection
    C. Property conservation (133)

6

99. Answer may include the following examples, but may include other appropriate examples approved by the instructor:
    A. *Nonintervention* — A pressure vessel exposed to fire cannot be adequately cooled so responders withdraw to a safe distance.
    B. *Defensive* — First responders evacuate the area, confine the hazardous material, and control ignition sources.
    C. *Offensive* — First responders evacuate the area and spray foam on a spill. (133, 134)
100. Defensive operations (134)
101. Offensive operations (134)
102. By respecting the material, noting the surroundings, observing the container, and eliminating ignition sources if the material is flammable (138)
103. A. *Weather* — Will wind shift (speed/direction), precipitation/humidity, air temperature, or sunlight affect the level of hazard present?
    B. *Topography* — Will the slope, altitude, or aspect have a bearing on the potential for the material to spread?
    C. *Water* — Does the incident affect — or have the potential to affect — oceans, lakes, rivers, streams, ponds, puddles, estuaries, flood control channels, storm and sewer drains, cisterns, reservoirs?
    D. *Occupancies* — Does the area of the incident include — or have the potential to spread to — public occupancies such as stadiums, churches, schools, hospitals, jails, and malls?
    E. *Community transportation systems* — Will the course of the incident affect depots, terminals, stations, and stops in the public transportation system?
    F. *Utilities* — Does the incident involve — or have the potential to involve — overhead and underground electrical transmission equipment, telephone and cable systems, natural gas, sanitary sewers, steam and chilled-water piping, cooling towers, or utilidors?
    G. *Zero energy state* — Has every power (electric, pneumatic, hydraulic, mechanical) or energy (chemical, thermal, gravitational) source that can produce unexpected movement of machines or containers been locked off, locked out, de-energized, adequately secured, or otherwise accounted for? (138, 139)
104. A. *Initial Isolation Zone* — The area AROUND the incident (including upwind) in which persons may be exposed to life-threatening concentrations of material.
    B. *Protective Action Zone* — The area DOWNWIND of the incident in which persons may become incapacitated and unable to take protective action and/or incur serious or irreversible health effects. (*ERG*)
105. The nature of the emergency, the route upon which they are to proceed, the location of the assembly area, and the approximate amount of time that they will be inconvenienced (142)
106. A. *Material considerations*
    - Toxicity
    - Quantity
    - Rate of release
    - Possibility of control
    - Direction of spread
    B. *Environmental conditions*
    - Wind direction
    - Temperature

- Humidity
- Precipitation
- Topography

C. *Population at risk*
- Population density
- Proximity
- Warning/notification systems
- Method of transport
- Ability to control
- Special needs (142, 143)

107. They should be directed to close all doors and windows and to shut off all heating, ventilating, and air-conditioning systems. (143)
108. If the vapors or gas is explosive, if it will take a long time for the vapors or gas to clear the area, or if the building cannot be closed tightly (143)
109. They prevent sightseers and other unauthorized persons from interfering with first responders; they help to regulate movement of first responders within the zones; and they minimize contamination. (144)
110. The staging area helps to keep responders and their equipment out of the way until needed; it minimizes confusion at the scene; it serves as a holding area for equipment waiting assignment. (145)

Chapter 7 Answers

DEFINITIONS OF KEY TERMS

1. *Aerated* — Mixed with air. (159)
2. *Breach* — Broken, ruptured, or torn condition. (156, Dict.)
3. *Diatomaceous earth* — A light siliceous material consisting chiefly of the skeletons of diatoms (minute unicellular algae) and used especially as an absorbent or filter; also called *diatomite*. (157, xvi)
4. *Dilution* — The application of water to a water-soluble material to reduce the hazard. (158)
5. *Miscible* — Ability of two or more liquids to mix together. (158)
6. *Polymeric* — Alcohol-resistant. (159)
7. *Proportioned* — Mixed with water. (160)
8. *Surfactant* — Substance added to some foams that enable the foam to shed, or separate from, hydrocarbon fuels. (163)
9. *Turbulence* — Irregular motion; particularly swirling, up-and-down air or water currents. (158, Dict.)

TRUE/FALSE

10. True (151)
11. True (154)
12. False. Confinement is primarily a *defensive* action. (155)

7

13. False. *Containment* is an offensive action that is performed at the *technician* level. (156)
14. False. *Confinement* is often performed before *containment* of the spilled material, although both can be started simultaneously. (155)
15. True (156)
16. False. Contaminated construction materials used in confinement *should be disposed of* properly. (157)
17. True (158)
18. True (158)
19. False. *Air-aspirating nozzles* produce a larger expansion ratio than do *water fog nozzles.* (158)
20. True (158)
21. False. Special foams for acid and alkaline spills *were limited to vapor suppression but were ineffective in suppressing fire and are no longer produced or sold.* (159)
22. False. The person trained to extinguish flammable liquid fires is *not necessarily qualified* to mitigate vapors produced by haz mat spills. (159)
23. True (161)
24. False. Foams designed for hydrocarbon fires *will not extinguish polar solvent fires regardless of the concentration used.*(161)
25. True (161)
26. False. Low-expansion foams are *least* effective when the fuel liquid exceeds 212°F (100°C). (161)
27. True (162)
28. True (163)
29. True (163)
30. False. Protein foam *must not* be plunged directly into the fuel. (163)
31. False. Alcohol-resistant fluoroprotein foams maintain their alcohol-resistive properties in solutions for about *15* minutes. (164)
32. True (165)
33. False. Hazardous materials vapor mitigating foam *is no longer commercially available.* (166)

MULTIPLE CHOICE

34. B (151)
35. A (158)
36. A (161)
37. D (161)
38. C (161)
39. B (161)
40. C (161)
41. D (161)
42. A (163)
43. C (163)
44. C (168)
45. B (169)

IDENTIFICATION

46. *Absorption* — Process of picking up a liquid contaminant with an absorbent (157)
47. *Defensive control* — Those measures used to contain or confine a material (157)
48. *Dilution* — The application of water to a water-soluble material to reduce the hazard (158)
49. *Foam quality measure* — Twenty-five percent drainage time and expansion ratio (158)
50. *(Foam) drainage time* — Time required for one-fourth of the total liquid solution to drain from foam (158)
51. *(Foam) expansion ratio* — The volume of finished foam that results from a unit volume of foam solution (158)
52. *Hydrocarbon fuel* — Petroleum-based fuel that floats on water (159)
53. *Polar solvent fuel* — Flammable liquids that are miscible in water (159)
54. *Protein-based foam* — Foams derived from plant or animal matter (163)
55. *Recovery* — Hazard removal and cleanup; the final priority of an incident (156)
56. *Subsurface injection* — Process in which foam is injected at the base of a burning storage tank and allowed to surface to extinguish the fire (164)
57. *Synthetic-based foam* — Foams made from a mixture of detergents (163)
58. *Vapor dispersion* — The action taken to direct or influence the course of airborne hazardous materials (158)
59. *Vapor suppression* — Action taken to reduce the emission of vapors at a haz mat spill (158)
60. *Venturi principle* —When a fluid is under pressure through a restricted orifice, there is a decrease in the pressure exerted against the side of the constriction, and a corresponding increase in the velocity of the fluid. Because the surrounding air is under greater pressure, it rushes into the area of lower pressure. (167)
61. *Expansion* — The ratio of final foam volume to original foam solution volume (160)
62. *Foam concentrate* — The raw foam liquid before the introduction of water and air, usually stored in a 5-gallon (20 L) pail, 55-gallon (220 L) drum, or an apparatus storage tank (160)
63. *Foam proportioner* — The device that introduces the correct amount of foam concentrate into the water stream to make the foam solution (160)
64. *Foam solution* — A homogeneous mixture of foam concentrate and water before the introduction of air (160)
65. *Finished foam* — The completed product after the foam solution reaches the nozzle and air is introduced into the solution (160)

66. Self-educting foam nozzle (167)
67. High-expansion foam generator (169)
68. Foam nozzle (167)
69. In-line eductor (167)
70. Balanced-pressure proportioner (168)
71. Around-the-pump proportioner (168)
72. Air-aspirating foam nozzle (169)

7

73. A. Control all ignition sources.
     B. Protect the material from excess heat, shock, or contamination.
     C. Confine material runoff as quickly as possible.
     D. Avoid contact with the material. (151)
74. Answer should contain any three of the following consequences:
     A. No apparent container damage
     B. Container damaged with no material release
     C. Container damaged with material release and no fire
     D. Container damaged with material release and fire (152)
75. Answer must be listed in the order below:
     A. Rescue
     B. Exposure protection
     C. Fire extinguishment
     D. Confinement
     E. Containment
     F. Recovery (152)
76. Answer should contain any four of the following factors:
     A. Nature of the hazardous material and incident severity
     B. Availability of appropriate personal protective equipment
     C. Number of victims and their condition
     D. Time needed (including a safety margin) to complete rescue
     E. Tools, equipment, and other devices needed to effect rescue (153)
77. Answer must be listed in the order below:
     A. Protecting the people
     B. Protecting the environment
     C. Protecting property not yet directly involved in but threatened by an expanding incident (154)
78. A. By building dams or dikes near the source
     B. By catching the material in another container
     C. By directing (diverting) the flow to a remote location for collection (155)
79. A. Covering with a fine spray (dust)
     B. Covering with earth (dust)
     C. Covering with plastic sheets or salvage cover (dust)
     D. Covering with foam (vapor)
     E. Directing with strategically placed streams (gas)
     F. Absorbing with water from hose streams (gas) (155)
80. Answer should include any five of the following factors:
     A. Material type
     B. Rate of release
     C. Speed of spread
     D. Number of personnel available
     E. Tools and equipment needed
     F. Weather
     G. Topography (156)
81. A. *The condition of the container* — Can the container withstand the stress of the operation? Will changes in material behavior, the weather, or other nearby operations further compromise the container?

7

B. *The properties of the material* — Will containing the material after a partial release be undesirable, especially if contamination has occurred or a chemical reaction has started? Will the operation cause first responders to come in contact with the material, and if so, what risk will that contact present? Is the material changing physical states?

C. *The rate of release* — Can the material be contained before the vessel is empty, or will the leaking stop soon because of the position of the breach? Are sufficient resources available for the size of the breach?

D. *The incident assessment* — Will the leaking materials ignite, explode, or react violently before or during the operation? Will containment devices and the container hold until recovery operations end? (156)

82. Answer may include the following three absorbents, but may include other appropriate examples approved by the instructor:
    A. Diatomaceous earth
    B. Sawdust
    C. Ground corn cobs (157)

83. Answer may include any five of the following examples, but may include other appropriate examples approved by the instructor:
    A. Crude oil
    B. Jet fuel
    C. Fuel oil
    D. Gasoline
    E. Benzene
    F. Naptha
    G. Kerosene (159)

84. A. Smothering prevents air and flammable vapors from combining.
    B. Separating intervenes between the fuel and the fire.
    C. Cooling lowers the temperature of the fuel and adjacent surfaces.
    D. Suppressing prevents the release of flammable vapors. (160)

85. A. Foam concentrate
    B. Water
    C. Air
    D. Mechanical agitation (aeration) (160, 161)

86. A. Pump
    B. Hose
    C. Foam proportioner
    D. Foam nozzle (166)

87. A. Operating the eductor at a lower pressure than that recommended by the manufacturer
    B. Gating down the nozzle (169)

88. Answer should contain any six of the following guidelines:
    A. Make sure that the eductor and nozzle are hydraulically compatible.
    B. Match the foam concentration listed on the foam container to the eductor percentage rating.
    C. If using an adjustable eductor, make sure to set it at the proper concentration setting.
    D. Use a hose capable of efficiently flowing the rated capacity of the eductor and nozzle.

7

E. Avoid kinks in the hose.

F. Avoid connections to discharge elbows.

G. If eductor is attached directly to a pump discharge outlet, make sure that the ball valve gates are completely open.

H. Make sure that the length of the hoseline does not exceed manufacturer's recommendations.

I. Open enough pails of foam concentrate to handle the task, and place them so that the operation can be carried out without interruption in the flow of concentrate.

J. Make sure that the bottom of the concentrate pail is no more than 6 feet (2 m) below the eductor. (170, 171)

89. Answer should contain any six of the following reasons:

A. Failure to match eductor and nozzle flow, resulting in no pickup of foam concentrate

B. Air leaks at fittings that cause loss of suction

C. Improper cleaning of proportioning equipment that results in clogged foam passages

D. Partially closed nozzles that result in a higher nozzle pressure

E. Too long a hose lay on the discharge side of the eductor

F. Kinked hose

G. Nozzle too far above eductor (results in excessive elevation pressure)

H. Mixing different types of foam concentrate in the same tank (172)

SHORT ANSWER

90. A. *Confinement* — The responder controls the flow of the haz mat spill and captures it at some specified location. (155)

B. *Containment* — The responder stops the further release of a material from its container. (156)

91. A. *Vapor dispersion*—The action taken to direct or influence the course of airborne hazardous materials (158)

B. *Vapor suppression* — The action taken to reduce the emission of vapors at a haz mat spill (158)

92. A. The identity of the material and its potential threat to life, the environment, and property

B. How much material has escaped from the container(s), if any, and the current condition of the container(s) (151)

93. The victim who can be most readily saved. (153)

94. A. *Fire exposure protection* — Structure or separate part of the fireground to which the fire could spread (*Orientation And Terminology* Glossary)

B. *Haz mat exposure protection* — People, property, systems, or natural features that are or may be exposed to the harmful effects of a hazardous material (*154*)

95. The size of the spill will increase. The runoff from the spill will increase. When these agents are used on burning tanks, the tanks could overflow and threaten adjacent containers. (154)

96. When personal or environmental risks are too great; when dealing with pesticide and flammable liquid fires in which the responder wants the fire to consume the fuel (154, 155)
97. To capture the moving materials as soon as possible in the most convenient location and to recover with the smallest amount of exposure to people, the environment, and other property (155)
98. A. Shovels may be used for building earthen dams and creating diversion channels.
    B. Salvage covers may be used for making catch basins.
    C. Charged hoselines may be used for creating diversion channels. (155)
99. The amount of water needed to reach an effective dilution increases overall volume and creates a runoff problem. This is especially true of slightly water-soluble liquids. (158)
100. The streams create turbulence, which increases the rate of mixing with air and reduces the concentration of the hazardous material. (158)
101. In terms of its 25 percent drainage time and its expansion ratio (158)
102. Except the special foams made for acid and alkaline spills (159)
103. A. *Foam is composed principally of water; therefore*, it should not be used to cover water-reactive materials.
    B. *Some fuels destroy foam bubbles; therefore*, a foam must be selected that is compatible with the liquid.
    C. *Water destroys and washes away foam blankets; therefore*, water streams should not be used in conjunction with the application of foam.
    D. *Foam cannot seal vapors of boiling liquids; therefore*, the material must be below its boiling point.
    E. *Some films that precede the foam blanket, such as those with AFFF, cannot be seen; therefore*, they may be unreliable and require reapplication. (159)
104. It forms a blanket on the surface of the burning fuel. The foam blanket excludes oxygen and stops the burning process. (160)
105. A. *Low-expansion foam* — Extinguishing liquid fuel fires; vapor suppression of unignited spills
    B. *Medium-expansion foam* — Confined-space fires
    C. *High-expansion foam* — Confined-space fires (163-166)
106. Steam caused by the vaporization of the foam in heated areas displaces gas and smoke, thus cooling the environment and extinguishing confined-space fires. (161)
107. A much lower application rate than is needed for ignited spills may be satisfactory for unignited fuel spills because radiant heat, open flame, and thermal drafts do not break down the finished foam as they would under fire conditions. (163)
108. A. They may be capable of supplying the correct application and flow rates but not have enough concentrate available to sustain the attack until the fire is extinguished.
    B. They may not be able to supply the foam rapidly enough to keep up with its consumption. (162)
109. A. *Line eductor* — Simple proportioning device that is attached to the hoseline or is part of the nozzle; uses the Venturi principle to draft foam into the water stream (167)

7

B. *Balanced pressure* — Proportioning system built into the fire apparatus pump; consists of a foam concentrate line connected to each discharge outlet and supplied with foam concentrate from a separate pump (167, 168)

C. *Around-the-pump* — Proportioning system built into the fire apparatus pump; consists of a small return line from the discharge side of the pump back to the intake side of the pump; an in-line eductor is positioned on the pump bypass (168)

110. Because they are fortified with fluorinated surfactants that enable the foam to shed, or separate from, hydrocarbon fuels (163)

111. A. The foam blanket immediately begins to drain water that floats on the fuel, sending an air-excluding film ahead of the foam blanket.
B. The fast-moving foam blanket moves across and insulates the fuel surface.
C. As the foam blanket continues to drain its water, more film is released, "healing" areas where the foam blanket has been disturbed. (165)

112. The slightest breeze may remove the foam blanket in sheets, re-exposing the hazard to stray ignition sources. (166)

113. A. *Basic in-line eductor operation* — Can be operated only at a fixed pressure and flow, using hose of a fixed size and length
B. *Variable pressure in-line eductor operation* — can be operated at a variety of pressures, thus allowing for adjustments in hose size and length and flow rates (167)

114. A. Operating the eductor at a lower pressure than that recommended by the manufacturer
B. Gating down the nozzle (169)

115. A. *Mechanical blower* — Air is forced through the foam spray; produces a higher air-content foam than water-aspirating generator and is typically associated with total-flooding applications
B. *Water-aspirating* — Air is pulled through the foam spray by water movement; typically produces a lower-volume foam than that produced by a mechanical blower (169)

116. See chart on the next two pages.

117. A. 2 pails
B. 8 pails
C. 47 pails (162 formula)

Type	Characteristics	Storage Range	Application Rate	Application Techniques	Primary Uses
Protein Foam	Protein based Low expansion Good reignition (burnback) resistance Excellent water retention High heat resistance and stability Performance not affected by freezing and thawing Concentrate can be freeze protected with antifreeze Not as mobile or fluid on fuel surface as other low-expansion foams	20°F – 120°F (-7°C – 49°C)	0.16 gpm/ft² (6.5 L/min/m²)	Indirect foam stream so as not to mix fuel with foam Alcohol-resistant must be used within seconds of proportioning	Class B fires involving hydrocarbons To protect flammable and combustible liquids where they are stored, transported, and processed
Fluoroprotein Foam	Protein based; fortified with fluorinated surfactants Fuel shedding Long-term vapor suppression Good water retention Excellent, long-lasting heat resistance Performance not affected by freezing and thawing Maintains low viscosity at low storage and use temperatures Can be freeze protected with antifreeze May be used with fresh or salt water Nontoxic and biodegradable after dilution Good mobility and fluidity on fuel surface	20°F – 120°F (-7°C – 49°C)	0.16 gpm/ft² (6.5 L/min/m²)	Direct plunge technique Subsurface injection Compatible with simultaneous application of dry chemical extinguishing agents	Hydrocarbon vapor suppression Subsurface application to hydrocarbon fuel storage tanks Extinguishing in-depth crude petroleum or other hydrocarbon fuel fires
Film Forming Fluoroprotein Foam (FFFP)	Protein based; fortified with additional surfactants that reduce the burnback characteristics of other protein-based foams Fuel shedding Develop a fast-healing continuous-floating film on hydrocarbon fuel surfaces Excellent, long-lasting heat resistance Fast fire knockdown Performance not affected by freezing and thawing Can be stored premixed Can be freeze protected with antifreeze Alcohol-resistant FFFP can be used on polar solvents at 6 percent solution and on hydrocarbon fuels at 3 percent solution Nontoxic and biodegradable after dilution	10°F – 120°F (-12°C – 49°C) Alcohol-resistant: 25°F – 120°F (-4°C – 49°C)	Ignited hydrocarbon fuel: 0.10 gpm/ft² (4.1 L/min/m²) Polar solvent fuel: 0.24 gpm/ft² (9.8 L/min/m²)	Must cover entire fuel surface May be applied with dry chemical agents May be applied with spray nozzles	Suppressing vapors in unignited spills of hazardous liquids Extinguishing fires in hydrocarbon fuels
Aqueous Film Forming Foam (AFFF)	Synthetic detergent based Good penetrating capabilities Spreads vapor-sealing film over and floats on hydrocarbon fuels Can be used through nonaerating nozzles Performance may be adversely affected by freezing and storing Has good low-temperature viscosity Can be freeze protected with antifreeze Can be used with fresh or salt water	25°F – 120°F (-4°C – 49°C)	Ignited hydrocarbon fuel: 0.10 gpm per ft² (4.1 L/min/m²) Polar solvent fuel: 0.24 gpm/ft² (9.8 L/min/m²)	May be applied directly onto fuel surface May be applied indirectly by bouncing it off a wall and allowing it to float onto fuel surface	Controlling and extinguishing Class B fires Handling land or sea crash rescue involving spills Extinguishing most transportation-related fires Wetting and penetrating Class A fires Securing unignited hydrocarbon spills

Type	Characteristics	Storage Range	Application Rate	Application Techniques	Primary Uses
Alcohol-Resistant AFFF	AFFF concentrate to which polymer has been added Multipurpose: can be used on both polar solvents and hydrocarbon fuels (used on polar solvents at 6 percent solution and on hydrocarbon fuels at 3 percent solution) Forms a membrane on polar solvent fuels that prevents destruction of the foam blanket Forms same aqueous film on hydrocarbon fuels as AFFF Fast flame knockdown Good burnback resistance on both fuels Not premixable	25°F –120°F (-4°C – 49°C) May become viscous at temperatures under 50°F (10°C)	Ignited hydrocarbon fuel: 0.10 gpm/ft² (4.1 L/min/m²) Polar solvent fuel: 0.24 gpm/ft² (9.8 L/min/m²)	May be applied direclty onto fuel surface May be applied indirectly by bouncing it off a wall and allowing it to float onto fuel surface	Fires or spills of both hydrocarbon and polar solvent fuels
Medium- and High-Expansion Foam	Synthetic detergent based Special-purpose, low water content High air-to-solution ratios (medium-expansion: 50:1 to 300:1; High-expansion: 300:1 or 1,250:1) Performance not affected by freezing and thawing Poor heat resistance Prolonged contact with galvanized or raw steel may attack these surfaces	27°F – 110°F (-3°C – 43°C)	Sufficient to quickly cover the fuel or fill the space	Gentle application so as not to mix foam with fuel Must cover entire fuel surface High-expansion foam usually fills entire space in confined space incidents	Extinguishing Class A and some Class B fires Flooding confined spaces Volumetrically displacing vapor, heat, and smoke Reducing vaporization from LNG spills Extinguishing pesticide fires Suppressing fuming acid vapors Suppressing vapors in coal mines and other subterranean spaces; in conceled spaces in basements As extinguishing agent in fixed extinguishing systems for industrial uses Not recommended for outdoor use
Class A Foam	Wetting agent that reduces surface tension of water and allows it to soak into combustible materials Rapid extinguishment with less water use than other foams Can be used with regular water stream equipment Can be premixed with water in the booster tank Requires lower percentage of concentration (0.1 to 0.5) than other foams (1, 3, or 6 percent concentrate)	25°F – 120°F (-4°C – 49°C) Concentrate subject to freezing but can be thawed and used if freezing occurs	Ignited hydrocarbon fuel: 0.10 gpm/ft² (4.1 L/min/m²) Polar solvent fuel: 0.24 gpm/ft² (9.8 L/min/m²)	Can be propelled with compressed air systems Can be applied with all conventional fire department nozzles	Extinguishing Class A combustibles

Chapter 8 Answers

DEFINITIONS OF KEY TERMS

1. *Bulk container* — Tank trailers, tank trucks, and rail tank cars. (185)
2. *Cartridge* — A case that contains an explosive charge for blasting. (176)
3. *Detonator* — A device or small quantity of explosive used to trigger an explosion in explosives; may also be called a *blasting cap*. (176, xvi)
4. *Dissipate* — To cause to spread out or spread thin to the point of vanishing. (178, xvi)
5. *Emulsion* — An insoluble liquid suspended in another liquid. (176, xvii)
6. *Etiological agent* — Infectious substance; microorganism or its toxin that causes human disease. (191)
7. *Exothermal* — Characterized by or formed with the evolution of heat. (188, xvii)
8. *Fissionable* — Capable of splitting the atomic nucleus and releasing large amounts of energy. (194, xviii)
9. *Flame impingement* — The point at which flames contact the surface of a container or other structure. (180, xviii)
10. *Half-life* — Time required for half of the atoms of a radioactive substance to become disintegrated. (194, xix)
11. *Pressure vessel* — Containers designed to withstand pressure; containers that hold compressed gases. (178, 179)
12. *Pyrophoric* — Material that ignites spontaneously when exposed to air; also called *air-reactive materials*. (189)
13. *Radiography* — Process of making a picture on a sensitive surface by a form of radiation other than light. (194, xxv)
14. *Radiopharmaceutical* — A radioactive drug used for diagnostic or therapeutic purposes. (194, xxv)
15. *Slurry* — A watery mixture of insoluble matter (such as mud, lime, or plaster of paris). (190, xxvi)
16. *Water gel* — Chemical solution that is gelled or partially solidified to make it easier to use or handle, for example gelatin dynamite (gelignite). (176, xxix)

TRUE/FALSE

17. True (175)
18. False. *Only properly trained personnel, such as bomb disposal technicians*, should handle, neutralize, or remove damaged or decomposed explosives. (176)
19. True (178)
20. True (179)
21. False. All pressure cylinders and pressure tanks made of metal are *steel*, except for disposable lift-truck types that can be made of *aluminum*. (180)
22. False. The U.S. DOT regulates all U.S. compressed gas pipelines *except for those on the consumer's property*. (180)
23. False. Flames from a pressure-relief device should *NEVER* be extinguished *as this may allow* flammable vapors to build up in the area and reignite violently. (182)
24. True (183)
25. False. Flammable *liquid* tanks, as opposed to flammable *gas* tanks, are not prone to BLEVE. (184)

8

26. True (185)
27. True (185)
28. False. The construction material used most extensively in rail tank cars is *steel, although some aluminum, stainless steel, and nickel alloy cars are in service.* (185)
29. True (185)
30. False. The vapors from flammable liquids are usually two or three times *heavier* than air. (186)
31. True (188)
32. True (188)
33. False. Spontaneously combustible materials can be either liquids or *solids*. (189)
34. True (190)
35. True (190)
36. False. Oxidizers mixed with *organic* materials can ignite spontaneously. (190)
37. True (190)
38. True (190)
39. False. Hydrogen peroxide solutions are shipped in tank cars made of *aluminum*. (190)
40. True (193)
41. True (193)
42. False. If a fire involving radioactive materials can be put out, first responders should do as *little* overhaul as possible after extinguishment. (195)
43. False. *Acids* have a pH of 1 through 6; Bases have a pH of *8 through 14.* (195)
44. True (195)
45. True (196)
46. False. Because of the density of corrosives, tanks used to transport them are *smaller* than those used for other types of liquids. (196)
47. True (196)

48. D (178)
49. A (179)
50. B (179)
51. C (181)
52. D (181)
53. B (182)
54. A (182)
55. A (182)
56. D (182)
57. B (182)
58. A (184)
59. A (186)
60. C (188)
61. D (189)
62. C (190)
63. D (193)
64. A (196)

8

MATCHING

65. H	73. E
66. A	74. A
67. C	75. F
68. F	76. B
69. G	77. D
70. B	78. G
71. E	79. C (176, 177)
72. D (175)	

IDENTIFICATION

80. *DOT* — Department of Transportation (175, xvi)
81. *CTC* — Canadian Transport Commission (179)
82. *CDC* — Center for Disease Control (194)
83. *API* — American Petroleum Institute (180)
84. *ASME* — American Society of Mechanical Engineers (180)
85. *BLEVE* — Boiling Liquid Expanding Vapor Explosion (182, xiii)
86. *SADT* — Self-accelerating decomposition temperatures (191)

87. B
88. A
89. G
90. B
91. G
92. B
93. A
94. G
95. B
96. A
97. G
98. A (194)

LISTING

99. Answer should include any four of the following examples, but may contain other examples approved by the instructor:
    A. Military installations/applications
    B. Mining
    C. Logging
    D. Construction
    E. Demolition (175)
100. A. Open flame
    B. Excessive heat
    C. Friction
    D. Impact
    E. Electrical shock
    F. Chemical contamination (175, 176)

8

101. A. Protect the cargo from contamination and shock.
   B. Reroute bystanders and traffic as the situation warrants.
   C. Control ignition sources.
   D. Review the shipping papers of the vehicle, and confirm this information with the driver/operator.
   E. Visually inspect the load for evidence of damage, spills, or leaks.
   F. Consult the appropriate technical specialists through the emergency contact telephone number listed on the shipping documents. Have the responsible party make the necessary contacts for transfer or disposal of the load. (177)

102. A. Gain control of the scene.
   B. Isolate the area.
   C. Initiate rescue, perform triage, treat survivors.
   D. Control fires that threaten remaining exposures. (178)

103. A. Pressure cylinders
   B. Pressure tanks
   C. Pipelines (179)

104. Answer should include any six of the following questions, but may contain other examples approved by the instructor:
   A. What gas is involved?
   B. What is the type and size of container involved?
   C. Is there mechanical damage to the container?
   D. Is there a leak?
   E. Is there fire?
   F. Is there flame impingement on the container?
   G. What is the availability of water?
   H. Can the fuel supply valve be shut off safely? (180)

105. Answer should be listed in the following order of importance:
   A. Execute any feasible rescues.
   B. Rely on the *ERG/IERG* for suggestions on evacuation distances.
   C. Determine wind direction and initiate evacuation downwind.
   D. Set up unmanned portable master stream nozzles to cool tanks and exposures (if there is a fire) and then have personnel withdraw to a safe distance.
   E. Do not allow anyone in or near the area until the arrival of specialists who have both the necessary technical knowledge and the resources to handle the emergency. (181)

106. A. Pressure-relief device operation
   B. Increase in (higher) sound pitch from pressure-relief valve
   C. Increase in pressure-relief valve torch height and volume
   D. Sounds of pinging, popping, or snapping metal
   E. Visible steam coming from tank surface
   F. Discoloration of shell; flaking of paint or metal from shell
   G. Bulge or bubble in tank shell (182, 183)

107. Answer should include three of the following examples, but may contain other examples approved by the instructor:
   A. Metal cans
   B. Metal pails
   C. Metal drums

8

    D. Metal tanks
    E. Pipelines (184, 185)
108. Answer should include any three of the following examples, but may contain other examples approved by the instructor:
    A. Paint thinners
    B. Solvents
    C. Camping fuel
    D. Motor fuels (184, 185)
109. Answer should include any three of the following examples, but may contain other examples approved by the instructor:
    A. Paint and hardware stores
    B. Residential garages
    C. Variety stores
    D. Service stations
    E. Wholesale outlets (184)
110. Answer should include any two of the following examples, but may contain other examples approved by the instructor:
    A. Bulk oils
    B. Thinners
    C. Cleaning solvents (185)
111. Answer should contain any five of the following tactics:
    A. Remove all ignition sources within a radius specified in the *ERG/IERG*.
    B. Apply a blanketing layer of foam to the liquid pool (at site or at collection area).
    C. Channel leaking liquids away from the incident scene and all exposures and to a collection point.
    D. Restrict water use to minimize runoff.
    E. Dike storm drains or manholes along the collection route.
    F. Notify the appropriate public works if any measurable quantity of the substance has entered the storm drain system. (186)
112. Answer should include any six of the following tactics:
    A. Lay initial hoselines.
    B. Establish a continuous water supply of sufficient volume to control the incident.
    C. Protect exposures.
    D. Notify additional resources as necessary.
    E. Evacuate, isolate, and control the incident area.
    F. Establish an incident command system.
    G. Control flowing liquid material. (186, 187)
113. Answer should include any three of the following examples, but may contain other examples approved by the instructor:
    A. Tubes
    B. Pails
    C. Steel drums
    D. Fiberboard drums
    E. Cardboard boxes
    F. Bags (188)
114. A. Is the material pyrophoric?
    B. Are there other materials nearby that are water reactive?
    C. What other chemicals are stored and how much?

8

  D. Can the area be isolated?
  E. Is everyone out of the area? (189)

115. Answer should include any three of the following examples, but may contain other examples approved by the instructor:
  A. Plastic-lined, multi-ply paper bag
  B. Metal tin
  C. Fiberboard drum
  D. Plastic drum
  E. Metal drum
  F. Stainless steel tank trucks (slurry-form) (190)

116. A. Physical contact with the material
  B. Inhalation of vapors
  C. Inhalation of material's products of combustion
  D. Contact with contaminated runoff water
  E. Contact with contaminated clothing (192)

117. Answer should include any three of the following examples, but may contain other examples approved by the instructor:
  A. Cardboard boxes
  B. Wooden crates
  C. Cylinders (compressed radiological gases)
  D. Metal drums (194)

118. Answer should include any two of the following examples, but may contain other examples approved by the instructor:
  A. Steel reinforced concrete casks
  B. Lead pipe
  C. Heavy-gauge metal drums (194)

119. Answer should include any three of the following examples, but may contain other examples approved by the instructor:
  A. Fissionable materials
  B. High-grade raw materials
  C. Nuclear fuels (both new and spent)
  D. Highly radioactive metals (194)

120. Answer should contain any five of the following containers:
  A. Glass bottles
  B. Plastic bottles
  C. Carboys
  D. Plastic drums
  E. Fiberboard drums (dry)
  F. Multilayered plastic bags (dry)
  G. Wax bottles (hydrofluoric acid) (195, 196)

121. Answer should contain any five of the following guidelines:
  A. Confine the spread of the material without coming into contact with the material or its vapors.
  B. Reduce vapor production with foam if applicable, or disperse or redirect vapors with fog streams, but do not let the water contact the spill or the container.
  C. Prevent the corrosive from reaching organic materials or other corrosives.
  D. Do not use water on spill or container.
  E. Cover the solid corrosives with salvage covers or plastic sheets to prevent scattering.

8

   F. Prevent corrosive from entering storm and sewer systems, creeks, canals, bayous, and rivers.

   G. Perform emergency decontamination for victims who have come in contact with the corrosive.

   H. Supply medical personnel with the name of the corrosive to enable proper treatment for victims. (196, 197)

122. Answer should include any three of the following examples, but may contain other examples approved by the instructor:

   A. Large-capacity highway tank trucks

   B. Rail tank cars

   C. Industrial storage facilities/processes

   D. Pipelines (183, 184)

SHORT ANSWER

123. A. *Poisonous materials* — Liquids and solids that are known to be toxic to humans or animals; Class 6, Division 6.1 materials

   B. *Infectious substances* — Microorganisms or their toxins that cause human disease (191)

124. A. A crystallized residue on the explosive

   B. The internal contents leaking through the container (176)

125. A. *Explosives not yet on fire, but threatened*
     Immediate concern — Protect endangered lives.
     Primary objective — Extinguish the fire and prevent the explosion. (177)

   B. *Explosives on fire*
     Immediate concern — Withdraw and protect life safety.
     Primary objective — Isolate the area, deny entry, and evacuate. (177, 178)

   C. *Nonflammable gas leaks not involving fire*
     Immediate concern — Protect life safety and exposures.
     Primary objective — Shut off the flow of gas. (181)

   D. *Nonflammable gas leaks involving fire or flame impingement*
     Immediate concern — Protect exposed tanks by cooling.
     Primary objective — Shut off the flow of gas. (181)

   E. *Flammable gas leaks not involving fire*
     Immediate concern — Prevent ignition.
     Primary objective — Shut off the flow of gas. (181)

   F. *Flammable gas leaks involving fire or flame impingement*
     Immediate concern — Protect exposed tanks by cooling.
     Primary objective — Shut off the flow of gas. (182)

   G. *Poisonous gas leaks not involving fire*
     Immediate concern — Protect life safety and exposures.
     Primary objective — Shut off the flow of gas. (183)

   H. *Poisonous gas leaks involving fire or flame impingement*
     Immediate concern — Protect exposed tanks by cooling.
     Primary objective — Shut off the flow of gas. (183)

   I. *Spilled flammable/combustible liquids not involving fire*
     Immediate concern — Prevent ignition of fuel.
     Primary objective — Stop the flow of fuel. (186)

8

J. *Spilled flammable/combustible liquids involving fire or flame impingement*
Immediate concern — Cool all exposures, including the tank itself.
Primary objective — Stop the flow of fuel to enable extinguishment. (186)

K. *Spilled flammable solids not involving fire*
Immediate concern — Prevent ignition of material.
Primary objective — Isolate and confine the material until it can be removed. (188)

L. *Spilled flammable solids involving fire or flame impingement*
Immediate concern — Cool exposures.
Primary objective — Control the fire by extinguishment or by controlled burning. (188)

M. *Spilled spontaneously combustible materials not involving fire*
Immediate concern — Keep the material wet.
Primary objective — Isolate and confine the material until it can be removed. (189)

N. *Spilled spontaneously combustible materials involving fire or flame impingement*
Immediate concern — Protect exposures.
Primary objective — Let the material burn until it is consumed. (189)

O. *Spilled dangerous-when-wet materials not involving fire*
Immediate concern — Keep the material dry.
Primary objective — Isolate and confine the material until it can be removed. (189, 190)

P. *Spilled dangerous-when-wet materials involving fire or flame impingement*
Immediate concern — Protect exposures.
Primary objective — Let the material burn until it is consumed. (190)

Q. *Spilled oxidizers not involving fire*
Immediate concern — Prevent ignition by isolating combustibles from the material.
Primary objective — Isolate and confine the material until it can be removed. (190)

R. *Spilled oxidizers involving fire or flame impingement*
Immediate concern — Protect exposures.
Primary objective — Control the fire by extinguishment or by controlled burning. (191)

S. *Spilled poisonous substances not involving fire*
Immediate concern — Confine the spread of the material.
Primary objective — Stop the flow and isolate the area. (192)

T. *Spilled poisonous substances involving fire*
Immediate concern — Confine the spread of the material.
Primary objective — Stop the flow, isolate the area, and let the material burn. (193)

U. *Spilled infectious substances not involving fire*
Immediate concern — Protect life safety and confine the spread of the material.
Primary objective — Isolate the area and deny entry. (193)

V. *Spilled infectious substances involving fire*
Immediate concern — Protect life safety and confine the spread of the material.
Primary objective — Isolate the area and let the material burn. (194)

   W. *Spilled radioactive materials not involving fire*
    Immediate concern — Confine the spread of the material.
    Primary objective — Isolate the area and deny entry. (195)
   X. *Spilled radioactive materials involving fire*
    Immediate concern — Confine the spread of the material.
    Primary objective — Extinguish the fire (if it can be done without risk to responder) or let the material burn out. (195)
   Y. *Spilled corrosive materials not involving fire*
    Immediate concern — Confine the spread without diluting the material.
    Primary objective — Shut off the flow, isolate the area, and deny entry. (196)
   Z. *Spilled corrosive materials involving fire*
    Immediate concern — Confine the spread of the material and protect exposures.
    Primary objective — Shut off the flow, isolate the area, and deny entry. (196)

126. Because they pose a long-term threat to the environment (178)
127. Disposable cylinders and some poison gas containers (180)
128. The municipal natural gas pipeline distribution system (180)
129. Metal can (184)
130. Stacked three or four high on wood pallets (184)
131. Metal powders, readily combustible solids that ignite by friction, self-reactive materials that undergo strong exothermal decomposition, and wet explosives (188)
132. The products of combustion from combustible solids are highly toxic; some materials, such as yellow and white phosphorous, can explode and scatter flaming fragments over a wide area. (189)
133. By hand, by scoop, by shovel, or with an extinguisher (189)
134. When the metal is reactive, when the metal is incompatible with the powder, when the first responder is untrained (189)
135. They are taught to immediately submerge the material in water. (189)
136. They are vented. (190)
137. Contaminants on the sole of a boot coming in contact with the oxidizer or the friction of stepping on the material can cause ignition, sometimes explosively. (191)
138. They have low self-accelerating decomposition temperatures and become explosive at high temperatures. (191)
139. In small vials that are measured in ounces (grams) and overpacked in strong containers for shipping (191)
140. A. *Type A packaging* — Contains low-level commercial radioactive shipments
    B. *Type B packaging* — Strongest packaging; can survive serious accidents and fire without release of radioactive material; used for radioactive packaging and shipment of more highly radioactive materials than those requiring Type A packaging (194)
141. A. *Time* — The shorter the exposure time, the lower the level of exposure.
    B. *Distance* — The farther from the source, the lower the level of exposure.
    C. *Shielding* — The more appropriate the shielding, the lower the level of exposure. (195)
142. Wax bottles; because the acid attacks glass (196)
143. It becomes corrosive itself after contact with the corrosive material. (196)

9 Chapter 9 Answers

DEFINITIONS OF KEY TERMS

1. *Absorption* — Process of picking up a liquid contaminant with an absorbent. (204)
2. *Chemical degradation* — Process of using another material, such as household bleach, to change the chemical structure of a hazardous material. (204)
3. *Contamination* — The transfer of a hazardous material to persons, equipment, and the environment in greater than acceptable proportions. (201)
4. *Decontamination corridor* — Corridor that runs from the hot zone to the cold zone in which decontamination procedures are performed. (205)
5. *Dilution* — Process of using water to flush the contaminant from the contaminated victim or object. (203)
6. *Exposure* — Process by which people, equipment, and the environment are subjected to or come into contact with a hazardous material. (201)
7. *Impervious* — Not allowing entrance or passage; impenetrable. (Dict.)
8. *Inert material* — Material that has no active properties; used as an absorbent. (204)
9. *Secondary contamination* — The contamination of people, the environment, or equipment outside the zone by a contaminant carried from the zone on workers' clothing or tools or in air currents or runoff. (202)

TRUE/FALSE

10. False. First responders at the *operational level* must be able to assist in decontamination techniques, which include selecting a decon site, setting up the corridor, and performing both basic and emergency decon. (201)
11. True (202)
12. True (202)
13. False. The *higher* the TLV, the less hazardous the material. (202)
14. False. Decontamination occurs in the *warm* zone. (203)
15. True (204)
16. False. The first priority in selection of a decontamination site is its *accessibility*. (204)
17. False. A cover should be used to cover the floor area of the decon corridor *whether or not the site surface is porous*. (205)
18. False. Water and *detergent* are the basic materials used for haz mat decontamination. (206)
19. False. *The use of such solutions require a higher level of training than that of the first responder*. (206)
20. True (206)
21. True (206)
22. True (209, 210)

IDENTIFICATION

23. *TLV* — Threshold Limit Value (202)
24. *TLV-C* — Threshold Limit Value-Ceiling (202)
25. *TLV-TWA* — Threshold Limit Value-Time Weighted Average (202)
26. *TLV-STEL* — Threshold Limit Value-Short-Term Exposure Limit (202)

27. Answer should contain any four of the following contamination methods:
    A. Walking in a spill
    B. Walking through a vapor cloud
    C. Touching the material
    D. Primary contact or penetration with haz mat dusts, particles, gases, fumes, vapors, or mists
    E. Secondary contact with contaminated tools, equipment, personnel, or runoff from the hot zone
    F. Contact with smoke and other products of combustion (201)
28. A. Accessible
    B. Speedy
    C. Economical (203)
29. A. Possibility of material being water-reactive
    B. Confinement and disposal problems (203)
30. A. Inexpensive
    B. Readily available
    C. Works extremely well on flat surfaces (204)
31. A. Does not alter the hazardous material
    B. Has limited use on protective clothing and other vertical surfaces
    C. Disposal may be a problem (204)
32. Answer should include any four of the following examples, but may contain other examples approved by the instructor:
    A. Household bleach (sodium hypochlorite)
    B. Isopropyl alcohol
    C. Hydrated lime (calcium oxide)
    D. Household drain cleaner (sodium hydroxide)
    E. Baking soda (sodium bicarbonate)
    F. Liquid detergents (204)
33. A. Reduced cleanup costs
    B. Reduced risk to first responder (204)
34. A. Time needed to determine the right chemical to use and to set up the process
    B. May create heat and toxic vapors that can be harmful to the first responder (204)
35. A. *Advantage* —Easier than trying to decontaminate
    B. *Disadvantage* — Can be very costly (204)
36. A. Accessibility
    B. Surface material
    C. Lighting
    D. Drains and waterways
    E. Water
    F. Weather (204)
37. A. Travel time in the hot zone
    B. Time allotted to work in the hot zone
    C. Travel time back to the decontamination site
    D. Decontamination time (205)
38. A. Barrier tape, safety cones, or other items to identify corridor
    B. Salvage covers or plastic sheets for floor surface covering
    C. Fire department catchalls, wading pools, or portable drafting tank for containment basin
    D. Drum or some other type of container for recovered materials
    E. Plastic bags in which to stow contaminated tools and personal protective equipment
    F. Low-volume, low-pressure hoseline (204, 205)

39. *Step 1:* Hose down the victim to remove the majority of contaminants from the victim and from any tools the victim is carrying.
    Step 2: Discard the victim's tools and equipment near the edge of the corridor.
    Step 3: Instruct the victim to step into the catch basin in the rinse area.
    Step 4: Scrub down the victim with detergent solution and water, giving special attention to areas that are easily missed: the folds in the chemical suit, under the arms, and in the crotch.
    Step 5: Instruct victim to step from the catch basin into the final area.
    Step 6: Working with another decontamination team member, remove the victim's clothing and equipment in the following order: 1) boots, 2) personal protective clothing, 3) undergloves, 4) SCBA.
    Step 7: Leave all clothing and equipment in the decontamination corridor for decontamination or disposal. (208)
40. A. Special protective clothing fails.
    B. First responder accidentally becomes contaminated.
    C. Victim needs immediate attention. (209)

SHORT ANSWER

41. The magnitude of an exposure is dependent on the duration of the exposure and the concentration of the hazardous material. When concentrations exceed the TLV-C for the material, it is considered a harmful exposure. (202)
42. The contaminant can be carried from the zone by worker's clothing or tools or in air currents or runoff. (202)
43. A. *Basic decontamination* — Removal of contaminants from workers' personal protective equipment and tools at a decontamination station/corridor in the warm zone (203, 208)
    B. *Gross decontamination* — First step of basic decontamination in which the majority of contamination is removed from the victim and the victim's equipment (208)
    C. *Emergency decontamination* — Physical process of immediately ridding dangerous contaminants from individuals on the spot, without regard for environment or property (209)
44. Persons exiting the hot zone can step directly into the decontamination corridor, thus decreasing the chances of secondary contamination and shortening the length of time it takes to get to and from the problem area. (204)
45. Anything that may accidentally get released in the decon corridor would drain into the contaminated hot zone and not into a clean area. (205)
46. Dike or place some sort of a barrier to ensure confinement of unintentional release and prevent accidental contamination away from the decon site. (205)
47. Cover the ground at the decon site with an impervious cover, such as a salvage cover or plastic sheeting, that will prevent the hazardous material from sinking into the earth. (205)
48. Adequate natural or permanent lighting where possible (205)
49. Set up a portable decon shelter, set up trailers at the scene, or perform decon in a remote building, such as a fire station, away from the site. (206)
50. Fire Protection Publications' **Hazardous Materials Response Team Leak And Spill Guide** and **Hazardous Materials: Managing The Incident** (207)

COMMENT SHEET

DATE ________________ NAME ____

ADDRESS ____

ORGANIZATION REPRESENTED ______________________________________

CHAPTER TITLE ________________________________ NUMBER _________

SECTION/PARAGRAPH/FIGURE _______________________ PAGE _________

1. Proposal (include proposed wording or identification of wording to be deleted),
    OR PROPOSED FIGURE:

2. Statement of Problem and Substantiation for Proposal:

RETURN TO: IFSTA Editor
                     Fire Protection Publications
                     Oklahoma State University
                     Stillwater, OK 74078

SIGNATURE _______________________________

Use this sheet to make any suggestions, recommendations, or comments. We need your input to make the manuals as up to date as possible. Your help is appreciated. Use additional pages if necessary.